REBEL
HALFBACK

JOE ARCHIBALD

J
Arlr

PHILADELPHIA

THE WESTMINSTER PRESS

The hissing showers at the end of the locker room began roaring like miniature Niagaras and muted the thinning racket outside the Westbrook Prep gym. Shouts of triumph, the hoot of horns, and the jangle of cowbells drifted up from the center of the town where police were already gently curbing the youthful hysteria that always followed a victory of the Westbrook Wildcats over Kent Valley.

Coach Buck Frazee allowed his players just three minutes in which to run wild. They milled around him in various stages of undress, many of them wearing only a towel around their middles. A helmet, flung toward the ceiling, came down and bounced off his head, and he let out a bellow.

"Those of you who haven't showered, get going. Those that have, get your clothes on before you get the sniffles. You'll need all you've got to be as happy as this a week from today. Don't leave this gym without first reporting to me. I want the trainer to look you over."

Larry Barstock, Frazee's star back, grinned at Blimp Crocker, the roly poly center. "Don't let 'em X-ray your stomach, Blimp, or they'll see those four chocolate bars you gobbled just before the game."

"You and your big mouth!" Crocker yelped. "He's only kidding, Buck."

"If I ever catch you breaking training, Crocker —" Buck Frazee turned his back on the fat boy.

"I'd better get my shower," Blimp said, momentarily subdued. He lumbered away, nearly upsetting Frazee's ends, which was something few opposing linemen had succeeded in doing since the start of the season.

"You should have a private dressing room, Blimp," Jim Westerman, the left end, called to him, "and a special shower in a garage."

Frazee looked at Larry Barstock's shoulder when the back came out of the showers. Three weeks ago, the trainer had been afraid of a partial separation of the acromioclavicular joint, the union of the collarbone and shoulder blade. Doc Stryker came over and explored with sensitive fingers for a few moments. "Not a thing seriously wrong, Buck," he smiled.

The coach said: "Fine, Larry. We'll want you at the peak against Canford." Frazee considered the welfare of his players above everything else. The recurrence of an injury, the coach knew, could be ten times worse than the original hurt. He would keep Larry out of the Canford game if there were any doubt of his condition, even though this might blast a hope the boy had nurtured for almost three years of winning selection to the Pundits.

The coveted prize was in Larry Barstock's mind as he slowly dressed. The fact that he had used Number Nine locker for the past three years seemed a good omen, for once it had been Big Bill Wardell's locker at Westbrook.

William C. Wardell had gone on to Kenton University and had become one of its greatest football stars. And every year since his graduation, for the past twenty years, he and other comfortably fixed old grads had named a prep- or high-school student to the Pundits, the most exclusive fraternity on the Kenton campus, and had underwritten the expense involved. It always had been understood that the boys chosen would some day pay this money back.

8

The Pundits had the right to reject the chosen candidate if they judged him inadequate after a three-week period of probation. The officers, although technically subordinate to a committee made up of Wardell and his associates, enjoyed a free hand on the campus.

The principles of the Pundits, as set down by Wardell and other charter members, were praiseworthy. The Pundits were to be the big brothers, the wise counselors who advised and assisted students in difficulties on or off limits. They were to be the natural leaders. They stood, in no snobbish sense, just a little above the crowd. They excelled in administration, character, and in athletics.

Wardell named his selection every year at the banquet held a week after the game settling the state prep-school championship.

Larry had three weeks to wait. The campus grapevine insisted he was being considered. *The Westbrook Wildcat* had been steadily building him up. His home-town paper had helped. His chances, he thought, were better than fair. So, he thought honestly, were Chuck Gorcey's of Canford.

Blimp Crocker, his morale fully restored, shouted above the showers' roar. Blimp was fat and jovial, a Friar Tuck, Junior, with a round, cherubic countenance, a fabulous appetite, and the deep resonant voice of a bullfighter. "You can't possibly miss, Larry. You're in. Two touchdowns against Kent Valley, and you kicked them dizzy."

"Sure," Corey, the blocking back yelled. "And such sportsmanship, Blimp. Picking up those Kent Valley boys and brushing them off after he'd smacked them down. That Venetti of theirs was sure a sweet ball carrier." He broke into song. "Oh-h-h, give me a ho-o-o-ome where the buffalo-o-o-o ro-o-oam, where the deer and the antelo-o-ope pla-a-a-y —"

"I wonder what Chuck Gorcey did against Hilltop," Willie Gaverstein, the quarterback, said as he splashed.

9

"Chuck's another sweet ball player," Larry said. "He's going to be hard to beat."

Blimp came out of the showers, the color of a boiled shrimp. "I wish I was the noble, deserving type. Imagine, a membership in the Pundits! What coach, especially at Kenton, would dare talk back to a protégé Big Bill Wardell had picked?"

Willie Gaverstein said: "Wardell had better pick Larry. Kenton has had two crummy football years. Even State licked them last year."

"I'd sure like to play under Hunk McQuade," Larry admitted. "I'd like to see him make a comeback."

"He will," Blimp promised grandly. "I figure on going to that seat of learning." He stepped up behind Larry who had gone to the mirror to comb his thick, brown hair. "Ah-h, Gregory Peck at seventeen! The lean-jawed, determined type. The real American boy, his eyes shining with hope for the future. The —"

Larry gave Blimp a dig with his elbow, and the fat boy grunted.

Buck Frazee took over and drained some of the cockiness out of his team. "You all think you're pretty good, don't you? You make certain mistakes against Canford that you made today and you'll regret them. You, Willie, waiting to kick on fourth down with the ball on your seventeen-yard line — calling for a running play on the thirty after you'd lost a yard on two tries against Kent Valley's line. Do you forget I taught you how to pass? Half of the line was charging too high — Corey, you played too far back on defense."

"Were we lousy?" Blimp whispered to Jim Westerman.

"Baumann, can't you ever get over the habit of wiping your hands on your jersey when you know you're going to carry the ball? Barstock, always remember to put both hands on the ball when you hit the ground after a hard tackle.

10

Crocker, you've got to get that ball away cleaner. They nearly blocked Larry's punt in the fourth quarter because of that high pass of yours. Now beat it, all of you. See you on Monday afternoon." The coach went out a side door of the locker room to the street.

"Pretty necktie, Dobie," Corey said to one of the reserve ends. "Where did you get the sport coat, Blimp?"

"Listen to 'em!" the fat boy snorted. "We beat Kent Valley for the first time in four years, and we tell each other how nice we look. Is this Vassar? Oh, dearie me, but you look simply stunning! Your hair-do, Willis, is just — "

A wet towel hit Blimp and knocked his shapeless slouch hat down over his left eye.

Buck Frazee came back for something he'd forgotten, and stopped and looked at his big center. "I'm glad you graduate next June, Blimp. I'm getting tired of convincing rival coaches that you're only seventeen and didn't vote for Hoover."

There was a gale of laughter in which Blimp Crocker joined.

Larry, Blimp, and Lew Corey left the gym and walked slowly along the curving concrete walk that led to the campus. The famous ivy-clad buildings of Westbrook were sprawled along an eminence that looked out over a valley of green farm land, through which wound the ribbon of silver that was the Pemigewasset River. Just beyond the valley was a long, low mountainside exquisitely arrayed in a riot of autumn's colors, softened by a thin, fall haze.

The trio stopped, and Larry said: "Persian and Turkish rugs spread out all over the place. I guess there isn't a prettier spot anywhere in the world."

"The UNO should have considered this place," Lew said. "Just standing here, a guy could never think of starting another war."

11

"Beautiful, sure," Blimp agreed. "But I'm hungry. You can't eat scenery."

"Kent Valley fed you plenty of it this afternoon," Larry chuckled. "You nearly choked to death on one divot you bit out."

Blimp sniffed. "You should be on the radio. They need comics bad. Well, I've got to do some studying tonight so let's get moving."

They walked across the campus, down into the town, and quickened their steps as they came in sight of Louie's Sugar Bowl, an institution at Westbrook. Blimp, in first, held up three fingers. "Your special pineapple parfaits, Louie!"

The place was packed. Louie beamed. "Hello, Blimp. Ah, eef you only had t'ree more brothers so beeg like you, I retire in five years an' go to Meeyami."

Westbrook high-school girls stared at Larry Barstock, slightly atomized. Larry settled into one of the booths near the wall.

Lew Corey said: "There's that cute one, Larry. The one named Maureen."

But Larry was thinking of Virgil. Latin was a tougher assignment than breaking through a strong defense. Big Bill Wardell expected a student's marks to be on a par with yardage gained. The triple threat was academic excellency, character, and athletic accomplishment. You failed in one, you threw the other two away.

"Stop worrying, Larry," Blimp said. "It won't be Chuck. You're as good as picked, like last year's apple crop." He looked over at the town's high-school belles. "Well, I guess education will have to wait until tomorrow. Lew, could I borrow your jalopy tonight?"

"No," Lew Corey said. "I have ideas of my own."

"A fine pal. Ask her has she got a friend."

"She has, Blimp, but wants to keep her."

"Very funny. Ver-r-r-y funny. And you call yourself a friend of mine? All right, here comes Louie, so give me elbow-room."

It was dusk when the three walked back to Trumbull Hall. A letter was on the table in the wide hall for Larry. Blimp Crocker found one addressed to him, in his father's handwriting.

"Funny," Blimp said. "I didn't write home for money. You think maybe the old boy wants to borrow some?" He ripped the letter open, read the contents aloud:

"'Dear Wally, write home at once. Your mother still remembers you. Dad.'"

"He must be a great guy," Larry smiled.

"Definitely a character, Larry. I'm a ba-a-a-ad boy! Your letter from a glamour girl back home?"

"The best I'll ever have," the star halfback said, and started upstairs.

Blimp said: "You'll want to read that all by your lonesome. I'll go and pester Lew for a while. I won't be long."

Larry went into a room simply furnished, and snapped on a light. There was a cot against each wall, a table and two easy chairs, a common dresser and a washstand. Pennants and a few pictures adorned the walls. On the table was an old aquarium Blimp had picked up in a secondhand shop in town, and in it was a chunk of a goal post taken from the Hilltop stadium. There was a piece of a green jersey Blimp had ripped off the back of a Blair ball carrier only a few weeks ago, and a tooth the fat center had lost against Dartmouth frosh. A sign leaning against the exhibit said: "THE CROCKER-BAR-STOCK COLLECTION. Please Do Not Handle Sacred Relics!"

Larry opened the letter from his mother.

"Dad has left for his lodge meeting, and Susan has gone to the movies, so at last I can write you without interruption. I had hoped to be able to surprise you with a little extra something this week, but our oil burner had to break down again and the repair man got the check instead. But I'm sure you have enough money to last you until the first of the month.

"Dad's situation at the factory has improved noticeably despite labor troubles and the shortage of raw materials, and only last night we thanked our stars over the fact that we have been able to see you through Westbrook with more than just the bare necessities. And Larry, if your dream of being named to the Pundits at Kenton comes true, it will be truly wonderful.

"But please don't set your heart on it too much. Let it be a marvelous surprise if it should come true, but do not feel bitter if you lose. You'll know you tried your best, and so will we. We are so proud that you are even being considered for the award. Dad sends his love, and if mine could be endorsed and honored at a bank, you'd be a millionaire."

Larry folded the letter and whispered good-by to the snappy sport shirt in the window of the Westbrook haberdashery, and to a week-end trip to Dixville Notch, and resigned himself to being a campus hermit until the end of the month.

Loud voices sounded in the hall, and Blimp and Lew Corey came into the room. The fat boy said gloatingly: "I talked him into it, Larry. She'll bring a friend, so how about you calling a number? Say, Maureen — "

Larry shook his head. "The Barstock dividend won't be declared for over two weeks. I've been reckless with the last one. Anyway, my date is with Virgil, and some math."

"Can I borrow your camel's-hair coat, Larry?" Lew asked. "I'll take care of it like it was my own."

14

"That's what I'm afraid of, Lew," Frazee's star halfback said wryly. He brought the coat from a closet.

"Maureen will be devastated," Blimp said sadly, and ducked the pillow his roommate threw at him.

When they had gone, Larry picked up his books and tried desperately to concentrate, but the name of William C. Wardell kept creeping through his mind. He wished that the banquet had come and gone, and hoped he would be a good loser if the Fates elected to pass him by.

On Monday afternoon the Wildcats were back on the practice field. The Kent Valley game had been a hard tussle and
the trainer had used a lot of rubbing oil and adhesive tape in
the locker room. Bone bruises and slight sprains had become
aggravated over the week end, and half a dozen players
limped as they trotted around the running track. Art Trevor,
the right tackle, wore a mask over his nose, and Willie Gaverstein's left ankle was tightly strapped. Frazee put his star
quarterback under wraps when light scrimmaging started,
and let the second-string field general call the signals.

Buck squatted and watched the first-string team push the
seconds down the field with a succession of running plays,
with Larry Barstock sparking the drive. He stood up quickly
and blew his whistle when a touchdown pass failed to click.

"Speed," he called to Kelsey, the left end. "When you
drift out for a pass, get it right in your mind that the defending back is standing there ready to nail you. Then cut the
other way at a forty-five degree tangent which will give you
a jump on the defending secondary. Never hesitate for a split
second or slow down, because if the pass is properly thrown
you can take it over your shoulder on the dead run. Go in
there and try it again."

Frazee kept the passers feeding the ends until the play did
click.

"And don't forget to cover your passes, all of you. When

the pass goes to the left, run that way in case of an interception. Kent Valley, you remember, intercepted on their sixteen and nearly upset your apple cart. A lucky thing for us that Larry overtook Venetti on the twelve-yard line."

"I would have had the guy back on the forty if I hadn't slipped," Joe Baumann grunted.

Buck smiled. "It was a beautiful interception by Venetti, Joe, and a nice run. All right, let's go. Humber, take Larry's place at left half. Larry, I want you to start booting. You've got a tough boy to kick against next Saturday. That Gregg lifted one almost sixty yards against Blair Academy without a breeze at his back. Kicking will play an important part against Canford."

Larry, walking over to the other end of the field with the coach, stopped to watch a stringy kid booting the ball at the uprights. The scrub holding the ball looked up at Buck and grinned.

"He's hot today, Coach. Sixteen out of twenty."

Frazee said: "That's nice. Keep kicking, Ellison." He knew the value of a point after touchdown. "All right, Larry, go to work." He tossed him a ball.

Larry began to boot. He boomed them out from the twenty-five-yard line, and angled them from the fifty, the forty, and the thirty-five toward the coffin corners. He booted until his leg muscles ached and sweat trickled down his face. Buck finally called him off.

"Pretty going, Larry. Run to the showers."

"Thanks, Buck."

"Wait," the coach said. "A bit of advice. I'd go and work on some Latin. I have to check on the marks all of the time, you know. Get Crocker to help you with math. He's got plenty of fat on him, but not much of it in his head."

Larry began to worry.

All that week Frazee drove his team. The championship

of the state hinged on the Westbrook-Canford game, and his whip cracked. Football fever raged through the New England town and the papers built up the tension. Larry began to hear the signals in his sleep.

Fifty-five, forty-one, hike! Thirty-three, sixty-seven, ninety-one —

He had always reveled in the contact of the game. The B team, looking for favor in Frazee's eyes, went at him. He laughed at them and rode on through. Frazee kept up a steady run of talk and punctuated it with blasts from his whistle. "Step on it! You think you'll get a chance to stop and pick violets running that ball against Canford? What have you got in your seat, Corey? Are anvils tied to you, Kelsey? Oh-h, did they throw that pass at you too hard, Jim? Get in there and dig."

Westbrook supporters paraded the streets with placards. BEAT CANFORD! SMOTHER CHUCK GORCEY! WE'LL CAN CANFORD! GO WESTBROOK, YOUNG MAN! There had never been a more potent display of pregame enthusiasm on any prep-school campus.

Adjusting his shoulder harness in the Westbrook locker room before the Canford game, Larry listened to the noise boiling out of the rapidly filling stands. The Canford players were already out there, limbering up and going through a mock signal drill. Big Bill Wardell, he knew, was in his seat on the fifty-yard line, right in front of the temporary broadcasting booth. Championship prep games were usually the contests that climaxed Big Bill's judgment of a student and an athlete. The sweat was already on Larry as he laced his shoes.

Buck's voice seemed far away. "I'm not going to preach. I've taught you all I know about this game, and I hope it's enough. You're ready — you're primed. Just remember that their weakness is pass defense, if they have a weakness. Play

18

it hard all the way, but play it clean, for your own sense of fair play as well as the penalties that come up. The starting team is the same line-up that started last week against Kent Valley, with one exception. Humber, you go in in place of Corey."

"I'm all right, Buck," Corey pleaded thickly. "This ankle isn't bothering me at all. I give you my word."

"Dry those tears," Frazee snapped. "You'll see action today."

Blimp Crocker banged a big fist into a palm. "Let me at 'em. All week I ate my hamburgers raw."

"I hope we get away with having two men at center, Coach," Larry said.

Blimp chuckled. "I just have big bones, Larry. How are you feeling?"

"Me?" Larry pulled on the heavy woolen parka. "Never felt better."

Nine thousand spectators stood up as one when the whistle blew. Canford kicked off to Westbrook, a soughing breeze at their scarlet backs as they defended the west goal. The new ball rose high and far off Gregg's toe, a pretty russet oval against the autumn sun.

The Canford ends came down, running like greyhounds after a mechanical rabbit. Larry took the impact of the leather against his chin and chest, tucked the ball under his arm and broke for the right side. He found a wall of scarlet in front of him and spun hard to shed a Canford tackler from his tight-fitting pants. He moved up the field ten yards — fifteen — twenty, and got to the thirty-four before they sent him crashing out of bounds. Westbrook lifted a booming cheer. Chuck Gorcey was the last man to get off Larry.

"I'm out to beat you, sweetheart," he warned.

"Keep coming, Chuck," Larry told him.

The backfield operating for Frazee was Baumann at full,

19

Larry Barstock at left half, Humber, the blocking specialist, at right half, with Willie Gaverstein calling the signals. Baumann carried for Westbrook and hit his head against a stone wall, losing a yard. The Canford team was husky, and their line outweighed the Wildcat forward wall. Willie Gaverstein faded back on the next play and Canford smelled a pass. But it was a lateral to Larry. Baumann and Humber wiped out the scarlet end and got Larry into the Canford secondary. Two hefty backs had him for a moment but could not hold him. Gorcey had to get Larry and he brought him down hard. Larry got up, little lights dancing in his eyes. It was close to a first down.

"Not through me, Barstock. Not this time," Gorcey said.

Larry felt good. Big Bill Wardell had seen that big gain. Clean all the way. He wondered how closely Wardell was watching Gorcey.

Willie led the team out of the huddle and barked the signals. He took the ball from Blimp Crocker, faked handing it to Larry, and plunged into the Canford line, throwing his little compact body over a guard's shoulder and clawing forward inch by inch before the play was considered stopped.

The line sticks were brought out. Larry, resting on one knee, nodded at Willie Gaverstein.

"Any part of the ball, Willie."

It was part of the ball. First down for Westbrook on their own forty-six and a half! The Wildcat cheering section howled and Larry struck off tackle and slithered from grasping, hungry fingers and churned his way forward for six more big yards. Canford supporters implored their team to hold. On the next play, Larry hit Canford right in the middle from a fake pass formation and went all the way to the scarlet twenty-nine before Gregg, playing safety for Canford, nailed him with a tackle that shook his teeth.

Canford asked for time out.

Blimp, panting like a Saint Bernard, dropped down beside Larry. "That Gorcey isn't a bad guy, I guess. But look out for him because he's tricky. The way he's playing, he's making them think we're very rough guys."

"You've got too much imagination," Larry chided. "Forget it. If we can score now, Canford will have to work uphill."

"We'll score," Blimp said. "Who has some gum?"

Lew Corey asked, "How many touchdowns has Gorcey made this year?"

"Eleven," Larry replied. "I need a couple."

Blimp said, "Give the ball to Larry, Willie."

"You want Buck to kick me out of this game?" Willie Gaverstein demanded. "Now's the time to pass."

The whistle blew. The Canford eleven, grim-jawed, lined up and dug in hard. Two fresh players bolstered their line. Willie Gaverstein calmly looked the situation over and called the signals. The ball was snapped to him nicely and he faked feeding it to Joe Baumann, who cut quickly in back of him. The left side of the Canford line shifted sharply to the left, and then Willie faded back and heaved the ball as straight and true as though it ran along a trolley all the way to the six-yard line. Jim Westerman got his hands on the ball, only to drop it. A crazy yell from the Westbrook stands broke off suddenly and resolved into a sickly groan.

"Give Larry the ball," Blimp choked.

Willie Gaverstein growled: "You can't click with them all, Blimp. Here we go again."

Willie took the pass from center and counted swiftly as he backpedaled. He leaped high and shot a short bullet pass over the line. Kelsey was there, taking it in the pit of his stomach and falling with it for a seven-yard advance. Canford lined up, expecting the aerial offense to continue. But Willie fed the ball to Larry, who came flying out from a single wing setup. Larry fairly rode Humber's rump as he catapulted through the scarlet forward wall to meet a swarm of tacklers. Hitting them in the middle, he dragged two of them to the seven-yard line with him. The Westbrook stands rocked and boomed with sound. Time was called. Canford players were not getting up; one of them was Chuck Gorcey. Quiet suddenly took hold of the field.

A voice that ripped the stillness apart roared: " Set 'em back fifteen! What, no penalty? What do you want, Ref, blood? "

" That louse, whoever said that," Blimp railed. Nevertheless he quailed a little at the booing. Gorcey was up now, being walked around by two of his mates. He stayed in and drew a tremendous ovation.

" An act," Blimp raged.

" Give me the ball, Willie," Larry said.

The quarterback grinned. " This close, it is always yours, Larry."

The Canford line stopped Larry on the three. On the next play it held on the two. Under the pile, Larry felt good, but stayed down to rest for a moment. He brushed Blimp's helping hand aside as he got to his feet. The Wildcat rooting section begged for a touchdown.

" You were always charitable," Willie Gaverstein said to Larry. " Let's give it to them."

Desperately Canford braced. Larry smashed into them and for a moment he seemed to have stopped dead at the scrimmage line; but the scarlet line buckled, then broke apart, and he dove over Baumann's broad back and scored. Buck Frazee immediately sent Ellison in to get the extra point. The kicking specialist split the uprights, and the Wildcat cheering section began tearing up the pea patch.

Now it was Canford's turn — Chuck Gorcey's turn.

Larry kicked off and the ball went all the way to the scarlet

22

five-yard line, too low and too hot for Gregg, the scatback, to handle. It bounded off his knee and shot upfield and he had to race against Frazee's streaking ends. Gregg threw himself on the pigskin a second ahead of Kelsey, and so averted catastrophe on the fourteen-yard line.

On the first play Chuck carried for the visitors, splitting between guard and tackle on the Wildcat's right side. He sifted through to the secondary and Larry, backing up the line, hit him and stopped him after a five-yard gain. Canford blockers tried to convoy the fast-moving Gregg around Westbrook's right end on the next play, but Gregg failed on a cut-in and lost two yards. Canford's quarterback had to think. Another running play was a gamble. A fourth-down punt might be blocked, and a pass would be suicide.

Canford huddled too long and drew a five-yard penalty, and so Gregg had to drop back and kick. He got away a beauty that went over Baumann's head. Baumann chased it and picked it up on his thirty-four-yard line where he was flattened in his tracks.

Westbrook rooters started yelling. "One more touchdown! Come on, team! One mor-r-re!"

A thrust through the middle that started from a spinner made six yards for Larry, but the horn called the play back. Westbrook had been off side and was set back five instead of going forward six. An end around lost three more when Baumann slipped just when it seemed he would make the sweep. Larry dropped back to punt. The pass from Blimp was low and he practically had to scoop the ball off the ground and hurry the kick, for the scarlet forwards were driving toward him. The ball left his toe and thudded sickeningly against the chest of a surging Canford guard, bounced away and rolled to the Westbrook three where Chuck Gorcey smothered it.

Canford rooters sent up a deafening roar.

"Tough," Larry yelled at Blimp. The fat boy's eyes filled and he banged a fist against his knee.

"So you're lousy," Willie Gaverstein said to Blimp. "Only last year they picked you for All-State Prep. Maybe you forgot. It's just the breaks, kid."

"I had plenty of time to get it off, Blimp," Larry said.

Frazee sent in substitutions. Two fresh linemen trotted in and Corey took Humber's place at right half for Westbrook. The Canford team, basking in the first joyous demonstration from their supporters, ran out of the huddle. Westbrook threw eight men into the line and Gaverstein, Barstock, and Baumann played up close. It would be Chuck Gorcey carrying the mail, of course — one hundred and sixty-eight pounds of Chuck Gorcey.

Canford touched Gorcey off. He came roaring in off tackle, a blocker in front of him. There was not much of a hole for him to go through, but he reamed it wide, wriggling through like a human corkscrew. He fought his way forward and was pulled down by Wildcat tacklers just across the last white line. Blimp Crocker slammed his helmet against a goal post and blamed himself for the score.

The scarlet eleven lined up quickly for the try for point, their cheering section still shrieking its delirious delight and drowning out Westbrook's pleading, insistent cry to block that kick.

Canford crossed up the opposition. A pass went straight and true into the arms of a Canford end standing deep in the end zone. The score was tied.

The game became a seesaw struggle, a duel between toes, Barstock's toe and Gregg's toe. Gregg made a little yardage on the exchange. The lines dominated the play and the plunging backs could not keep up a concerted drive. Willie Gaverstein threw a scare into the opposition when he hit Jim Westerman with a long pass on the Canford twenty-two-yard line. But Willie's second try via the air was intercepted on the Canford eleven, the runback by Gorcey being liquidated on the Westbrook forty-six. The half ended with that play.

CHAPTER
3

Westbrook players poured into the dressing room. Blimp plopped down on a bench and groaned.

"I give 'em that tie like it was already Christmas, Buck."

Willie Gaverstein laughed at him as he pulled off his sodden jersey. Others joined in the laughter and Blimp's spirits rose. Buck Frazee chewed slowly on his gum and gave thanks for a team that could carry one another's load. He watched the trainer check bruises, was satisfied that his first string was intact, and consulted his notes.

"All of you listen to me," he said. "I'm satisfied for the most part with your game so far. They got the first big break and capitalized. One thing you blockers want to watch is that side-swiping. It verges pretty close to clipping, and once out there I thought we'd get nailed for fifteen yards. You're not giving Willie enough protection on his passes. In the line, I want to see you working under your opponents more. Remember, Ackerman, if a Canford blocking back is working toward the inside, you can be pretty sure the play is inside. Get more speed into the line and always try to stay on your feet. A man stretched out on the ground is useless."

The coach swung toward Blimp. "You admit you made a mistake. When you go back out there, Blimp, keep that motto for all good centers in your head: 'Not too high, not too low, not too fast, not too slow.' I think that's all."

Blimp sidled over to Larry. "That Gorcey!" he said bitterly.

"What about him?"

"I wish I was sure. I think he's taking somebody for a ride. Maybe you. Maybe Big Bill Wardell. He can make himself look better than he really is. He puts on an act that he's being roughed up. I've seen guys like —"

"In your hat," Larry scoffed.

Frazee became interested in the retaping of Corey's ankle. He then began to check on shoulder and hip pads and shoes. On the other side of the partition, the Canford players could be heard buzzing like a swarm of bees. Larry caught Gorcey's voice; there was a timbre to it that warned the Wildcats to throw everything they had left into the second half.

Buck glanced at his watch. "All right, go out and take this game."

A freckled boy came into the locker room and asked for the Westbrook coach.

"Here, son," Buck called out.

The boy handed him a note. "I took one to the Canford coach. He gimmie a quarter."

Buck dug down. "Racketeer!" he said. He opened the note and read it aloud to the players: "'Good luck, Westbrook. May the better team win. W. C. Wardell.'"

Larry's blood tingled. Running along in front of the stands a few moments later, he looked up and saw Big Bill in a big gray coat, holding a pair of field glasses. He knew that Wardell was a keen observer and wouldn't miss the intricacies of a single play. One touchdown, Larry thought, would possibly be the difference between Canford and Westbrook, between Barstock and Gorcey.

The third period was a standoff, the irresistible force against the immovable object. Three mild scoring threats petered out inside the forty-yard line stripes. Once Baumann fumbled just when it seemed the Canford line was beginning to wilt under the Wildcat smashes. Once on the offensive,

27

on his own thirty-one, Gregg, of Canford, catapulted into the line from a fake kick formation and broke through to meet Larry coming up. Larry nailed him and threw him hard. Gregg seemed a little wobbly when he stood up again, and the scarlet adherents booed.

After that play Chuck Gorcey knifed his way deep into the Wildcat secondary where Larry pulled him down. Gorcey stayed down for over a minute, then got slowly to his feet, rubbing the back of his neck.

The Canford rooters protested again. " Give them an ax! " a stentorian voice roared.

Larry looked at Blimp and shook his head. The announcer's voice reached across the field. "Tackled by 66. Barstock! "

Big Bill, Larry knew, was right under that mike.

Gorcey was forced to boot, for Gregg had been taken out for a while. He was no Gregg, and his kick was hurried. The ball went out of bounds just short of the fifty-yard line.

Willie Gaverstein snapped: " Stop clowning. Now we move! "

Westbrook employed the single wing for a weak-side play. Larry took the ball from Willie, stepped back as if to pass and drew the defensive end in deep. The interference formed, and he slanted toward the outside. Baumann and Corey cleared a path for him into Canford territory, where Gorcey knifed in seemingly from nowhere to bang him down. A spinner picked up six more yards with Baumann carrying. Canford again asked for time out.

Blimp and Willie Gaverstein went over and stretched out on the grass beside Larry. The water boy ran up and Blimp said: " Come here, Gunga Din. My throat is like a dried mackerel." He swished cool water around in his mouth and let just a little of it go down into his stomach. "We have got to score this time, Willie."

"About two minutes left in this quarter," Larry said.

When the teams lined up again, Willie Gaverstein began working from a double wing, mixing his plays. A reverse inside tackle, outside tackle. A spinner and then a double reverse. A cross buck and then the fullback off tackle. The Canford defense kept backing up until they found themselves on their own eighteen-yard line. Twice, Chuck Gorcey had been the only player between the Wildcats and a touchdown. He was doing his job and doing it well.

Canford, sensing a pass, lined up in a 6-2-2-1 defense.

Willie said in the huddle: "We throw the works right here, pals. Old Seventy-five."

The roaring crowd could not keep their seats. Willie held up a hand pleadingly for a little quiet. The ball came back to him and he spun around and faked it to Corey. Larry, teaming up with Baumann, took the ball from Willie, and faked a plunge into the line at Baumann's heels. The big fullback opened a hole just as Larry put on the brakes. He was supposed to pass to Westerman, but he saw that the end was blanketed. Without hesitating, he took off again and smashed through a closing gap.

Chuck Gorcey seemed to spring right out of the ground. Larry straight-armed him and sent him sprawling. Baumann, plowing ahead, dumped two scarlet-jerseyed tacklers, and Larry rode over them to the ten, to the five, to the last white line, and into pay dirt. The Wildcat band began to play the Westbrook Victory March.

Players danced around Larry and slammed him on the back. Blimp gave him a bear hug and yelled: "Yeah, maybe the big guy is watching Gorcey out there. Chuck's sitting on the ground and pulling up grass."

"I was lucky," Larry said. "They had the play figured, so I had to gamble. I couldn't have made it click without Baumann."

29

"Sure," said Joe Baumann. "But the writers will call it alertness, Larry."

Again Frazee sent Ellison in, and again the specialist paid off, his boot registering the fourteenth point for the Wildcats. Westbrook cheer leaders threw their megaphones high into the air.

Larry kicked off to Canford. Gregg, back in for the scarlet, took the kick on his eleven, hesitated for a brief instant until his interference formed, and then cut suddenly for the left side line. Gorcey, coming from that way, took a flip pass and legged it for the right side. The Westbrook tacklers had to shift, momentarily shocked by the old and tricky maneuver. Gorcey was flying. He passed the twenty-five-yard line, the thirty, the thirty-five. It was Larry Barstock who drove him out on the forty-three just as it appeared he would go all the way. The Canford back rolled all the way to the Canford bench after he was hit. Once more, he got up slowly, and once more Canford booed.

"Slick baby," Blimp growled. "He's playing psychology with us, Larry. An act, I tell you."

Larry felt a doubt creep into his mind as he watched Gorcey trot back into action. Even the Westbrook stands gave him a cheer.

Time was running out. Teamed up, Gregg and Gorcey began to puncture holes in the Westbrook line. Reaching midfield, the Canford quarterback elected to gamble, and faded back and threw a long pass out into the flats. The scarlet end, hemmed in by alert Wildcat defenders, was bumped as his fingers made contact with the ball. Baumann batted it down, but the officials ruled interference, for the second bad break against Westbrook.

Canford started to yell once more. Their team was on Westbrook's nineteen. Buck Frazee sent in four new linemen, took Corey out, and sent in a good defensive right half named Kyle. Westbrook lined up in a 7-2-2 defense. This box defense was weak against passes, but Willie Gaverstein was sure Canford would stick to the ground. Thus far, Canford's aerials had gained very little.

Willie went up and down the line banging his boys on their rumps, talking to them, encouraging them. The visitors snapped out of the huddle.

Gorcey sleeved sweat from his face. He came in behind two blockers from a double reverse setup and crashed over right tackle and was going full tilt when he hit the secondary. The stands were screaming. It looked as if Gorcey was shaken loose until a jet bomb wearing the Westbrook jersey hit him. Gorcey went high into the air and was deposited on the turf with a loud thump. The ball squirted out of his arms and there was a snarl of players on the twelve-yard line. When the players were unpiled, Westbrook's end, Kelsey, was on the ball.

The announcer droaned: "Tackled by Barstock, number 66. Fumble recovered by Kelsey of Westbrook."

Gorcey stayed down. His teammates swarmed around him. Three Canford players, tempers on edge, rushed toward Larry, and Blimp Crocker spilled them by simply throwing himself down in front of their feet. Canford supporters railed and ranted and booed.

Blimp yelled: "If he's hurt, I've got a figure like Bacall. Tell him to stop being a possum and making Larry look like a mug. What did Gorcey expect, a kiss?"

The officials quickly restored order. Chuck Gorcey went out of the game amid a thunderous ovation. He walked off slowly.

"He put it over, I'll bet," Blimp almost wept.

Westbrook began their offense. Willie tried a quarterback sneak that gave him only half a yard and then, in the huddle, suggested that they play it safe. Larry dropped back into punt formation, and this time Blimp's pass was perfect. Canford's forwards came charging in desperately. Larry kicked the ball off the right shoulder of Canford's left tackle. It was a powerful boot that brought a roar from the stands. The ball sailed over the fifty-yard line and kicked up lime on the Canford thirty-eight where the safety man for the scarlet let it roll. The ball bounced back toward the fifty and came to rest on the forty-three.

"Only three minutes left," Willie told his team after checking with an official. "They've got to pass. And here comes Gorcey again, now they've got possession. Nice hand he's getting."

Canford's quarterback also knew that the only chance his team had to score was through the air. He began pitching and his first attempt was grounded. A Westbrook defender had his fingers on the second try, but failed to hold it. Canford went into punt formation, but the Westbrook team knew there would be no kick.

Willie Gaverstein called out, "Watch it!"

The scarlet employed the single wing. Their halfbacks, Larry diagnosed, were going to serve as decoys to draw Kyle and himself toward the side lines, so that the Canford ends could slip in behind them. The pass came from center. The scarlet backs faded toward the left, but Larry stubbornly refused to be drawn out. He was covering the Canford receiver when the ball finally came flying out of Gorcey's fingers. The pass was short and Larry cut in and took it on the dead run. It was Gorcey who had to run him out of bounds on the Canford twelve-yard line.

"That should do it," Blimp yelped, slapping Larry on the back. "It looks like Buck's taking us out."

Wildcat reserves swarmed in. A roar of sound fanned out from the Wildcat rooting section as Frazee's first-line operators jogged off the scarred gridiron. Buck got up from the bench and told them he was proud of them all.

Wrapped in blankets, Blimp and Larry sat side by side and watched the reserves kill time with three running plays. Willie's replacement deliberately took a five-yard penalty for delaying the game. Fourth down for Westbrook with seven big yards to go for a first down. There were only seconds left on the clock. The Westbrook reserve pivot man was about to get down over the ball when the gun went off. An official picked up the pigskin, and the Wildcat team whooped shrilly and danced around as the disconsolate Canford team trotted off.

The locker room was pandemonium. Buck wanted to talk, but saw he would have to wait. Blimp and Joe Baumann lifted Larry up bodily and deposited him atop a locker. The demonstration was still at fever pitch when the big broad-shouldered man in the gray ulster came in. A wet towel, aimed at Willie Gaverstein, nearly got him, and Larry's heart went into a tight spin for a moment.

But Big Bill Wardell smiled as he shook hands with the coach and congratulated him. He slapped Westbrook players on the back as he wormed his way toward Larry. Larry's knees gave a little as he gripped Wardell's hand.

"You played a mighty fine game, Barstock. I wish you luck. They could use you at Kenton." Wardell turned and walked out, and waved at them before he shut the door.

Buck waited until all of his players had taken their showers and dressed. He said, as they grouped around him: "You're a great bunch of fellows, and I'll hate to say good-by to a lot of you next June. I think you're the greatest team I ever coached here, temperamentally and physically. You gave me all you had and never grumbled. I want to thank each and every one of you. Drop in and see me during the winter months." He looked at Larry. "I'd like to see you for a few minutes in my office."

Blimp said, "We'll wait outside, Larry." His voice was thick and his eyes were much too bright.

Larry followed Frazee up a flight of stone steps. Buck said, "Sit down, Larry." He stuffed a pipe with tobacco and set it going. "I've never talked much about this Wardell award business; I've never been altogether in favor of inducements. But if it's coming to you, and if you think it will help you at Kenton, I want to say that you deserve it."

Larry's throat was tight. "I'll admit I've been working for it."

"I know," the coach said. "But remember that nothing is ever sure, Larry. It is pretty difficult sometimes to understand a man's judgment, even Big Bill Wardell's. There are little quirks and prejudices inside the heads of us all, and sometimes we can be influenced by the most insignificant developments. You can make the grade at Kenton without help from anyone, so take everything in stride, win or lose. Thanks for making this team what it was the past two years. And if at any time, for any reason at all, you need help, don't hesitate to call on me."

Larry nodded. "I'll remember. You're a great guy, Buck. I —"

Buck said quickly: "Skip all that, Larry. Beat it. They're waiting for you."

Blimp, leaning against the side of the gym, said to Lew Corey: "What do you think about that Gorcey? The way he acted this afternoon —"

"I'd forget it," said Corey. "I wouldn't mention it again to Larry. Hold everything; here he comes. As I was saying, Blimp," he said in a louder voice, "if we get into another war, and we could easily enough if people keep shooting off their mouths, we could turn you over to the War Department.

In a few years you'd be armored. Presto — a Sherman tank! Hello, Larry; we thought you stayed for a cup of tea."

"Step on it," Blimp said. "I want a couple of hamburgers."

Westbrook Prep students still snaked up from the gridiron and across the campus, brandishing fragments of the goal posts. They carried an effigy labeled CANFORD toward the place of sacrifice where, at dusk, the bonfire would be touched off. Scattered groups, under the ancient elms, sang old Westbrook songs in the dying day.

Larry, crossing the campus with Blimp and Lew, was silent with the thought that with the passing of another year all this would be but a memory. Still silent, he led the way toward the town and Louie's place.

Three hundred places at the long tables in the Westbrook gym were filled the night Buck Frazee's championship team was honored, the night Big Bill Wardell was to name his candidate for the Pundits at Kenton. Wardell was a square-jawed man, with very little silver showing at his temples, who looked hard enough and fit enough to play a full quarter against the Redskins or the Packers.

The mayor of Westbrook was on Wardell's right at the head table and Buck was on his left. Along the table were the board of trustees of the town, the editor of *The Westbrook Times,* and half a dozen prep-school coaches. Chuck Gorcey, of Canford, and Nick Venetti, of Kent Valley, were with groups from their respective schools.

Samuel J. Farrington, the principal of Westbrook sat with members of the faculty at a side table. He had written Wardell declining to spoil the evening for the football players. He was quite sure, he said, that they saw enough of him around the campus and that festivities in the gym should center around the game of football.

"Snappy dresser, that Wardell," Willie Gaverstein said across the table reserved for the Wildcat team. "Think I'll look as sharp when they make me president of the bank back home?"

Blimp ate another stalk of celery, a roll, and a dozen olives.

"I saw him looking this way a couple of times, Larry. Want to make a bet?"

Larry shook his head. "And leave my butter alone."

The food was brought in. The main course was turkey and the good things that went with turkey. There was enough ice cream to top it off even for Blimp. The toastmaster stood up and the hum of talk quickly died.

Blimp whispered, "If he's reminded of a story, I will throw the sugar bowl at him."

". . . and so it is only fitting that we hear first from the gentleman who *is* Westbrook Prep, even though he chose to put himself in the background tonight. He has guided the destinies of this institution for over twenty years, and I hope and trust he'll be with us over twenty more. His stern countenance, let me assure you, is only a mask, a defense mechanism to hide his real softness. I am honored to introduce the headmaster of Westbrook Preparatory School, Samuel J. Farrington."

Dr. Farrington stood up, smiled, characteristically tugged at his coat lapels and cleared his throat.

"A great old guy," Blimp said, and Larry took a stalk of celery away from him.

"What I have to say, gentlemen, will take up very little of your time," the principal began. "I extend a warm welcome to the boys from other schools, and I have a special message for those from Canford and Kent Valley. I sincerely hope our turkey has compensated for our having beaten you on the football field."

Prexy waited until the applause tapered off.

"Looking at you, I am certain we are going to get that better world we read so much about, and I know you won't let down certain men who lost their lives in this last war. I refer particularly to fifty men who prepared at Westbrook.

They played out there on the football field, sat in the same classroom seats that you Westbrook boys are using now. They had bright hopes for the future. Let us not forget them. I can hear certain voices still — and certain laughter. God grant that the hardest battle any of you will have to fight for many years to come will be over the possession of a football."

"A better world," Blimp mumbled. "They should make better cookies than these too."

"My three minutes are up," Dr. Farrington said smilingly. "We have an honored guest here and I understand he will have quite a lot to do with the success of this occasion. I know you are impatient, but first I want the toastmaster to call on the gentleman who is responsible for the laurels the Westbrook team wears tonight. He is more than a football coach."

The toastmaster brought Buck Frazee to his feet and the Westbrook team lifted a burst of sound that shook the big windows. Buck, giving his boys ninety-nine per cent of the credit, asked every member of the team to stand and take a bow. The applause for Larry Barstock was a spontaneous roar.

The toastmaster took over once more. "And now we come to a man who needs no flowery introduction. We already know what he accomplished on the gridirons of Westbrook and Kenton University, and of the success he has made beyond those fields. It gives me great pleasure to present to you William C. Wardell."

Big Bill stood up. The acclaim was deafening, and he gestured for silence. He began to speak as the dwindling echoes of the applause brushed against the ceiling and along the walls.

"This is it, Larry," Blimp said huskily.

"Relax, boys," Big Bill began. "I'm more nervous than any of you. First, I want to say that I watched the Canford-Westbrook game very closely. It was fought as hard as any game

38

I've ever seen. I felt those tackles myself." He paused at the ripple of restrained laughter.

Larry Barstock hoped his ears did not look as red as they felt.

"Football," Big Bill continued, fingering the golden emblem he wore on a chain strung across his vest, "is truly the game that dissects the characters of the boys or men playing it. Watching them, you get a pretty good idea of the way they'll play the game of life. I remember players who tried too hard, great players at that, who used the game as a means to an end and forgot the fun that was in it. Often they counted their chips during play, and afterwards — " He suddenly raised his hand. "No, I do not intend to give you a sermon and tell you that you are custodians of the future. I hate platitudes and smugness."

"I'm sold on him," Blimp chuckled.

"Gag him, Larry," Willie Gaverstein said.

"When we consider a candidate for the Kenton Pundits," Wardell went on, "we are not in the least bit interested in whether he comes from a one-room shack or from the governor's mansion. Of course, I've had a hard time convincing some people of that. Naturally I leave myself open to criticism no matter what choice is made. There is always talk of favoritism and discrimination, for you won't ever change human nature.

"I've never felt sorry for any man as long as I was sure he had two hands and a good, clear mind. The man who was born with a silver spoon in his mouth is sometimes at more of a disadvantage than the one forced to start from scratch." Big Bill's mouth twitched. "Not that I wouldn't have picked the silver spoon for myself if I'd had anything to say about it."

There was applause and a ripple of laughter.

"But there is really great satisfaction in battling the odds.

Ask any member of the Kenton team of five years ago. They won only one game on the schedule, but it was an upset over Vail, a highly favored team."

Blimp leaned close to Larry. "That Gorcey looks pretty sure of himself," he whispered, and reached for another macaroon. Larry fidgeted in his chair, and Blimp added in a low voice, "Why don't the big guy talk about how he made All-American?"

"Pipe down, Blimp." Larry's fingers dug into the tablecloth. This was the zero hour. He knew Wardell had come to the point at last.

"Now about the Pundits," Big Bill said, and once more there was a terrific round of applause that slowly trailed off to a tense stillness. "As you all know, the only collateral I require is what I see in a boy. If the three things are there, then he is my choice. They are character, academic efficiency, and athletic ability. I don't mind telling you that it has been very difficult for me to decide this year, and not until the game between Westbrook and Canford was played did I make my choice."

Wardell gave Larry a glance. His eyes sought and found the eager faces of Gorcey and Venetti.

"The boy I have chosen knew what it was to play against the odds and beat them," Big Bill said. "He has shown me he has all the requirements."

Larry stiffened in his chair.

Blimp whispered incredulously, "Why, he's looking at you, but what he said doesn't seem to fit you."

The quiet in the gym seemed to have definite body.

Big Bill said, "It is my great privilege to name Kenneth (Chuck) Gorcey of Canford Preparatory School to the Pundits of Kenton University."

There were a few quick gasps of surprise, but these were

40

drowned out by the applause that shouldered along the walls and caromed off the high ceiling. Big Bill motioned to Gorcey to rise.

Blimp said under his breath, " It's a raw deal, Larry."

The Westbrook team seemed stunned.

Chuck Gorcey stood up and, when the hand clapping ceased, said in a happy, quaking voice: " Mr. Wardell, I — I don't know what to say. I really don't deserve the honor, but I'll do my best at Kenton."

" Listen to the faker," Blimp growled. " Larry, where are you going? "

Larry hurried across the room and offered his hand to Gorcey. Again the applause was deafening.

Gorcey said, " Tough luck, Barstock."

" Good luck, Chuck," Larry said. He went back to his place and sat down.

Big Bill Wardell congratulated him on his sportsmanship. " I hope you'll go to Kenton, Barstock, for I have an idea if you don't I'll never dare set foot on that campus in the Berkshires again. The best of luck to you all, and my only regret is that I can't send the whole bunch of you to the Pundits. It has been wonderful to be here tonight."

Larry broke away from the table with the Wildcat team and found it difficult to hide his disappointment.

Buck Frazee caught him by the arm near the door. " Keep your chin up, Larry," the coach said quietly. " Some day you may have a chance to show Wardell he picked the wrong guy."

Blimp Crocker snapped: " It was that act of Gorcey's. The poor, downtrodden, persecuted kid. We picked on him. He kidded everybody but me, Buck."

" Pay no attention to him, Coach," Larry said, and tried to smile.

41

"I'd go to Vail," Blimp still railed. "I'd show the big stiff."

Buck laughed and moved away. He knew Blimp, a good kid with a big bark and practically no bite.

People kept reaching for Larry, stopping him and telling him they thought he should have had it. Outside, a contingent of Canford students were putting on a demonstration, with Chuck Gorcey in the middle of it. Larry got Blimp by the slack of his pants as the fat boy showed signs of moving toward the group.

"All right," Blimp sighed. "Let's go and get a hamburger."

"We've just been to a banquet," Willie Gaverstein reminded him.

"That turkey? It's still stuck in a cavity in one of my back teeth. You can't expect a growing boy to exist on rolls and limp celery! They half-starve us, and then double-cross us. It shouldn't happen to a dog."

"The Pundits!" Lew Corey sniffed. "So what, Larry? They're just overgrown Boy Scouts. I looked 'pundits' up in the dictionary last night. They're supposed to be learned men, and most of them were Brahmans, originally."

"Never heard of that frat," Blimp said. "Well, I'm glad it's all over."

Larry nodded. "You know something, guys? I feel the same way, kind of relieved. I'm almost glad now that Chuck got the nod."

"Frank Merriwell, I do declare," Blimp snorted. "You got a brother named Dick?"

"You should know, Blimp," Willie Gaverstein said. "You read 'em only a couple of years ago."

"Me?" Blimp said, scandalized. "My favorite fiction, I'll have you know, was more adult, more stimulating to an adolescent mind. I read *Deadwood Dick* and *Stage Coach Robbers*."

42

Ten days later *The Westbrook Wildcat* carried a bitter editorial by Jerry Pool, its editor.

"We naturally must assume," Pool wrote in part, "that Larry Barstock lacks at least one essential qualification for the Pundits at Kenton U., but for the life of us we cannot isolate it. Perhaps Mr. Wardell can tell us what it is."

Blimp Crocker, reading the editorial in Lew Corey's room, chuckled gustily.

Larry said: " I wish Jerry hadn't written that stuff. It makes me look like a sorehead."

"Wardell has it coming to him," Willie Gaverstein said flatly.

"I still can't get over the way Wardell looked at Larry when he knew he was picking Gorcey," Blimp said, shaking his head. "As though he was wondering if he wasn't pulling a boner. You think Big Bill will see a copy of this paper? "

"If I find out anyone here sent him a copy, I'll let all the air out of him," Larry threatened.

"What are you lookin' at me for? " Blimp said in an aggrieved voice.

"I just don't like the look in your eyes, Blimp," Larry said. " I think I'll duck over to my room and write some letters."

"Haven't you something to do, Blimp? " Lew Corey asked pointedly.

Blimp shook his head. " No, Lew, I like it in here."

"Everybody clear out," Lew said. "Where do you think I get my sleep? "

"In Latin class, mostly." Blimp grinned. "You got any candy, Lew? "

The trees of Westbrook had shed their brown and brittle leaves and the first snow fell. The Canford game and Wardell's choice were now of the past, and students in the dorms crammed late to assure themselves of a hearty welcome when they arrived home for the Christmas holidays. But Blimp's moon face lengthened as the days shortened.

"We should make him see a doctor, Larry," Jerry Pool said a week before Christmas. "There was a Grable picture at the Elko this week and Blimp didn't leave Trumbull Hall. I tell you, it's serious."

Larry Barstock slanted a glance at Willie Gaverstein. "Don't any of you get it? He comes from Minnesota and can't go home for the holidays. Tonight, I'll invite him to come home with me. Mother and dad say they'll be tickled to have a guest. Let's find Blimp."

They located Blimp slumped down in a chair near the billiard table in Trumbull.

Lew said: "I can't wait until I get home, Larry. A twenty-pound turkey, and ma always gets first prize at the county fair for her mince pies."

"We prefer pumpkin at our house, Lew," Larry said. "Golden brown, with lots of nutmeg and other spices. And fruit cake? Oh-h-h my! Then there's the oyster dressing in the turkey —"

Blimp catapulted out of his chair and reached for a pool cue. " I'll murder both of you wise — ! "

" A fine thing! " Larry cried. " A fine way to act when I'm about to invite you to have Christmas dinner with me."

" What's that, Larry? " Blimp gulped. " Listen, old friend, I'm not myself. Did I hear you say — " Blimp's face cracked into a beatific grin. He let out a war whoop, picked Larry up by the waist and lifted him high off the floor. " Lo-o-ve that ma-a-a-an! "

" When did you first find out that you two cared? " Willie Gaverstein asked, cracking wise to hide what he really felt.

Sleet rattled against the windows of the day coach heading south to Springvale, Connecticut, Larry Barstock's home town. Blimp Crocker tried to become interested in a magazine digest, but soon dozed off. Larry pored over a nonfiction book, *Our Future and the Atom.* At Springfield, Massachusetts, the train lurched to a stop and Blimp woke up suddenly.

Several passengers got on and two boys settled into the faded plush seat behind Larry and Blimp. One heaved his suitcase up on the rack. It slid off and hit the back of the seat and tumbled against Blimp's head.

" Watch it, pal," he said.

The passenger's eyes were cool. " Sorry; an accident."

" Forget it," Blimp said. The train drew out of the station, and he asked, " How is the book, Larry? "

" Pretty deep stuff," Larry said. " The world's sure in a mess."

Blimp shrugged. " It's the people in it. The rocks and rivers, the trees and mountains never change. Just look back to when they went out to dig gold in the Klondike. A lot of 'em froze to death, or got shot. Then there were the forty-niners who started for California in covered wagons. A lot of 'em never got there. It took about a hundred years to get a lot of gold out of the ground, and when they got it, what did they do with it? They dug a big hole at Fort Knox and buried it again."

Larry chuckled.

"And why bother to go to college? Gossip columnists, band leaders, and crooners get paid more than a United States president. Corny comedians and movie stars get a hundred times more a year than surgeons who can operate on a heart or a brain. Nobody's ever satisfied. A millionaire rides by in a limousine and sees a husky laborer eating a Dagwood Bumstead sandwich and wishes he had the guy's stomach. The laborer wishes he had the millionaire's money —"

"Ah, the poor man's philosopher," a voice behind Blimp said. "Get a soap box."

Larry and Blimp twisted around in their seats. Blimp said: "Never mind the box, pal; give me the soap. My mother writes she can't get any in the stores."

A middle-aged man across the aisle chuckled.

Larry said, "Quiet, Blimp."

"Who asked them to listen?" Blimp demanded.

"We couldn't help it, my friend," a smooth voice answered. "You would never need a megaphone. Have you an opinion on the Darwinian theory?"

"Not until you guys came along," Blimp countered.

Larry said: "Take it easy, Blimp. They're just trying to needle you."

"Quite a joker, isn't he, Herb?" the smooth voice said. "Quite a joker."

Suddenly Blimp leaned toward Larry and spoke in an undertone. "I got a look at that suitcase up there. It has a Kenton sticker on it. And the initials, 'H.K.R.'"

Larry's eyes began to widen. "'H. K. R.,'" he repeated

softly. " Blimp, I had a feeling I'd seen him before. He's Herb Rossiter. He played for Kent Valley our first year at West-brook, and now he's first-string halfback for Hunk McQuade. If they decide to use the needle again, we're taking all they hand out. Use your head. You're going to Kenton."

Blimp sank lower into his seat.

When the train stopped at Hartford, one of the Kenton students took down his bag. "See you after the holidays, Herb." His overcoat slipped from his fingers and smothered Blimp. "Sorry," he said, yanking it off the fat boy.

"Think nothing of it, pal," Blimp said. "I like it."

"You look a little familiar to me," the departing passenger said. "Or is this a bad dream?"

Larry's temper suddenly quickened. "You've had your fun, haven't you? Let's drop it."

"You know," the Kenton student said, "your face looks familiar too. Maybe I'll see you again."

"Maybe you will," said Larry.

When the train pulled out of the station, Rossiter leaned forward. "No hard feelings, I hope. That was Mel Jardin, editor of *The Kenton Opinion*. Not a bad fellow when you get to know him. He likes to explode time-honored theories. He said to me: 'They say stout people are always jolly and can take a ribbing. Let's find out.'"

"Someday," Blimp growled, " a guinea pig will bite a chunk out of him."

"My name's Herb Rossiter."

Larry offered his hand. "I'm Larry Barstock. This is Blimp Crocker."

The fat boy shook hands grudgingly.

"I knew I'd seen you before, Barstock. You sent me out of my last game with Kent Valley with a twisted knee. Tough break your not getting the call for the Pundits."

47

Blimp sharpened his own needle. " Quite a team you had at Kenton this year and last. Even the Rhode Island Aggies tied you six weeks ago. What has happened to Hunk Mc-Quade? "

There was a short uncomfortable silence in the seat behind.

" I'll tell you," said Rossiter. " We've been waiting until you arrive, Crocker. Just marking time. How about you, Barstock? I heard you were going to go to Vail to help pin Big Bill Wardell's ears back."

" *The Kenton Opinion?* " Larry asked, thinking of Jardin.

" I hear Vail is considering dropping Kenton from its schedule," Blimp cut in. " I should write Vail's coach and promise him real competition."

Rossiter laughed. " You seem to forget we're getting Chuck Gorcey next year. The pick of the preps, isn't he? "

" *Touché,* " Larry complimented. He was glad when the train pulled into New Haven. " Come on, Blimp. We change here."

On the platform he glared at the fat boy. " The wrong foot. Both wrong feet."

" Didn't they ask for it? " Blimp asked defiantly. " Of all the trains coming this way they had to pick the one we were on. Well, don't expect me to try and pick up spilled milk. I'm no tomcat."

The Barstock sedan met them at the Springvale station. Larry's father clamped his hands over his son's shoulders. " You look good, boy. You sure look good."

Susan, fourteen, stared at Blimp. Mr. Barstock swung around quickly and held out his hand. " So you're Blimp Crocker? We've certainly heard enough about you. Glad to have you with us, Blimp."

Larry said: " Go ahead, Susan. Shake hands with Blimp."

Susan's laugh sounded like the tinkle of sleigh bells. " How do you do, Blimp? You don't mind if I call you that? "

"All my friends do," Blimp said, a little embarrassed.

But he beamed when he met Larry's mother. There was just a touch of silver in her brown hair, done up the way he liked it. Her smile took all the Minnesota homesickness out of him. Being here, he felt all at once, was almost as good as being in his own house. She was, he thought, more than Larry's mother. She was any guy's mother if the need should arise.

Dinner produced lamb chops and mashed potatoes, green peas and cauliflower, three kinds of pickles, and spiced pears. All of Blimp's nostalgia faded away with his second helping of lemon meringue pie. Susan kept consulting her wrist watch and looking from Larry to Blimp.

"There's an awfully good picture at the Olympia tonight, Larry," she said hopefully. "But I guess you don't feel like going after a long train ride."

"Right, Sue," Larry said. "I feel like stretching out somewhere."

"I'd like to go," Blimp said quickly. "That is, if you're — "

"Why don't you and Blimp go, Susan?" Mrs. Barstock urged.

"I'd love to go," Susan said, jumping up. "We have just time to catch the first show. I'll get my things."

When Susan and Blimp had gone, Larry went into the living room with his father. "Leave the dishes until later, mother, and we'll help you with them," Tom Barstock called over his shoulder. Larry stretched out on the sofa. His father carefully clipped the end off a cigar and leaned back in his favorite chair.

For a while neither spoke. Finally Tom Barstock said: "All right, Larry, let's talk about that award business. Still disappointed?"

"I'm just about getting over it, dad," Larry said. "I wish everyone else would."

49

"Why do you think Wardell passed you by?"

"Either I lacked one of the requirements, or Big Bill saw in Chuck the underprivileged kid he once was. Perhaps he thought of the battles he'd had, and of how he'd have welcomed a lift at one time. I'm not blaming Wardell one bit. I most likely would have done the same had I been in his place."

Tom Barstock did not remember when a cigar had tasted better. "I knew you'd take it that way. Still want to be an electrical engineer?"

Larry sat up. "They've turned out some good ones at Kenton."

"Then stick to it," Tom Barstock said. "I'll be able to see you through without any trouble."

"I wouldn't swap you for Big Bill," Larry said, his throat tight. "I'm going to get a job next summer. Perhaps I'll see Mr. Davidson while I'm home."

"You mean you want to tote bags of cement and lumber?" his father asked, taken aback. "I could make a place for you at the office."

"You don't need me there, dad. I could get in swell condition in that lumberyard. I certainly wouldn't get muscles in my shoulders and drive in my legs holding down a desk. You have to be in top shape to make a Kenton team, even the frosh. Nearly three hundred guys come out for football and the coaches can only pick about three teams from that number."

"Football," Tom Barstock said. "O. K., if that's what you want. It's a part of college and I wish I'd had it."

Larry shrugged. "Maybe I won't even make the freshman team." He stood up and glanced at his watch. "Wonder how Blimp and Susan are making out. Blimp's no glamour boy, and unless you understand him —"

"Susan," Tom Barstock said dryly, "is really adequate, Larry."

Mrs. Barstock came in and stood close to Larry, laid her head against his shoulder. "What do you think of our son, Tom?"

"All-American, sure," Tom Barstock answered.

"I've only got one thing against my parents," Larry grinned. "They gave me a thick skull. Calculus, they tell me, is tough. The mortality rate in that subject is wicked."

The dinner dishes were finished when Blimp and Susan came in. Blimp said: "They had a moth-eaten newsreel with shots of the Kenton-Vail game. Are they bad! Strictly from Limburger. We would have held them almost even at Westbrook. Say, why didn't you wait for us so's we could help with the dishes? Didn't I say to you, Susan, we should hurry back?"

"So he had another pineapple parfait," Susan laughed. Her cheeks were rosy and her eyes sparkled. Blimp was good for people, Larry thought. He made them happy. A dozen Blimp Crockers could do more to insure international harmony than a gross of stiff-necked ambassadors.

The Barstocks knew they were going to have the happiest holiday in Springvale.

Late that night Larry went into the guest room where Blimp was ah-ing and oh-ing the soft bed as though he had never before seen a bed. All at once Blimp became serious. "You shouldn't ever beef about not getting named to those Pundits, Larry," he said. "Not with all you've got. If Gorcey never had parents like yours, then I'm tickled Big Bill Wardell made it up for him. If he never had a home like this and a sister like Susan — well, he had something coming to him."

"I guess I've never realized just how lucky I am, Blimp," Larry said seriously.

"That little round red hat of Susan's," Blimp sighed. "Her hair the color of preserved pineapple. She's as sweet as a parfait . . . No, no; she's sweeter. That hat's a cherry topping it off. Go away, pal, and don't disturb me. Let me dream."

CHAPTER
6

In the prep student's book, the year is divided into four seasons: football, basketball, baseball, and vacation. After Larry and Blimp returned from the Christmas holidays the days seemed to fly, possibly because they were beginning to realize that a golden chapter in their lives was coming to a close. Westbrook songs carried a deeper meaning; Westbrook friends seemed more dear; and slowly they began to brace themselves for the shock of parting.

In Louie's Sugar Bowl one night, Larry and Blimp and Willie Gaverstein discovered that their thoughts were running in the same channel.

"Just last night," Blimp said, "I got to thinking."

"We'll take your word for it," Willie told him.

"Last year at the alumni dinner the same thought struck me," Blimp went on, unabashed. "We graduate from here and go to college, and after that we go to work, and after that we get old and lose our hair. And then we're gone."

"That was a quick life, Blimp," Larry laughed.

"Those old-timers should stay away," Blimp grieved. "It's bad for us psychologically. Last year there was one old-timer here who looked just like I'm going to look when I'm seventy. I get nightmares over it."

"Don't forget," Willie Gaverstein observed, "that most of the old grads have been through two wars and as many depressions. It's surprising to me they're in such good shape."

"I think we're about as lucky as we can ever hope to be," Larry said seriously. "For four years the kids who left Westbrook knew they were going to war within a few months. No matter how tough it'll be when we're through school, it'll be nothing compared to what they had to stack up against."

Blimp scooped more ice cream. "You think there won't be another war?"

"That's what I think, and I'll keep on thinking it," Larry said. "If everybody did that, there surely wouldn't be another one."

"I don't get it." Blimp looked at Willie.

"Don't ask me, Blimp," that student said. "I'm no crystal-gazer."

Blimp took a long deep breath. "Well, only about seven weeks more and then — *kaput!* We'll be alumni. Ex-Westbrook football heroes. Is that good?"

"Seems like it's been a long time, Larry," Willie said. "Yet it seems that only yesterday you walked into my room and said, 'I'm Larry Barstock from Springvale, Connecticut.' We'll shake hands, a lot of us, after we get the diplomas, and say, 'So long,' knowing we'll never see each other again."

"Don't feel so sad, Willie," Blimp said. "I'm going to dear old Kenton U. with Larry. I'm stuck with him once more."

"You and Gorcey on the same team," Willie Gaverstein said to Larry, and shook his head.

"Think we'll beat Canford today with Merrick pitching?" Blimp asked. At the moment baseball was closer than football.

"If we do, we'll have to hold a certain guy hitless," Willie said.

"Always Gorcey," Blimp sighed. "He's everywhere. I'm awful sick of hearing about him."

Larry said, "He's hitting .396 for the season."

For Westbrook Prep the game was the last one of a dismal

baseball season. Canford had beaten them three weeks before, 11–2, and Chuck Gorcey had hammered out three hits. Today, fifteen hundred spectators were in the stands when Merrick toed the pitching slab and faced Canford's lead-off man. Larry was in right field, and Willie Gaverstein was behind the plate. The presence of the old grads, back for commencement, acted as a stimulus, and at the end of the sixth inning there was not a run on the narrow scoreboard for either team.

In the top of the seventh Merrick walked a man after two were down. Chuck Gorcey stepped in, worked the count to three and two, and then laced a hard drive to deep left that was good for a triple and drove in the first run of the game. A single scored Gorcey, after which Merrick settled down and struck out the Canford second baseman.

The score remained 2–0 until the last half of the ninth. Westbrook came in for her last try, and the first batter reached first base on an error by the Canford shortstop. Willie Gaverstein fouled out to Chuck Gorcey, who was catching. The Wildcat center field, Humber, struck out, and Larry stepped in to see what he could do to keep his school in the ball game. He looked at two bad ones, and took a called strike. He smashed the next pitch through the box for a single. The runner on first reached third in a cloud of dust, and when the ball dribbled away from Canford's hot-corner guardian, Larry streaked for second and slid in safely. A single now would tie up the game.

Lew Corey worked the string out against the tiring Canford hurler. He hit the three and two pitch on a line into short right, and the man on third scored easily, but the spectators saw that the play on Larry would be close. The ball came in to Chuck Gorcey on a long bounce just as Larry hit the dirt. Gorcey was crowding the plate, and Larry had to slide through him. Gorcey did not budge an inch.

The umpire signaled that Larry was out, and a disappointed wash of sound sighed from the Wildcat rooting section. Gorcey walked toward the bench, taking off his catching tools. Blimp, who had watched the game from the bench, yelled, "Larry's hurt!" and made a dash for the plate.

Larry tried to get to his feet. His face was white and warped by a grimace of pain. Between Willie Gaverstein and Blimp, he tested the knee he had twisted. He said: "It's bad, guys. Let me down for a minute."

Chuck Gorcey came back to the plate and looked down at Larry. "We keep getting in each other's way, don't we, Barstock?"

Blimp looked sourly at the Canford star. "Forget you weren't playing football, Gorcey?"

"What does that mean?" Gorcey demanded angrily.

"Not a thing," said Blimp. "Not a thing."

Larry was helped off the field.

"It's probably only a slight twist," Willie Gaverstein said. "We'll get the word from Doc Stryker in a little while."

Larry was on the table for a half hour before the doctor gave his verdict. "I want you to come to my office Monday morning, Barstock, if the pain doesn't ease up. At the moment I doubt if an X-ray is necessary, but keep off that leg and rest as much as possible."

Buck Frazee, coming in while Larry was getting the feel of the crutches, noticed the little beads of sweat around the boy's mouth, the fear in his eyes.

Larry said: "Hello, Buck. I guess I should have kept out of baseball."

"Don't let anything build up inside your head," the football coach said sharply.

But Larry's face remained bleak. "These knee injuries can bother a guy all his life. I remember cases where — "

"You're young," Buck snapped, "and that's three fourths

of the cure for anything. Willie and Blimp are out there waiting for you. Get out to them before they blow their tops."

Larry found Blimp sitting on the grass outside the gym, gnawing at his fingernails. Willie Gaverstein was tossing pebbles at a knothole in a tree. Blimp struggled to his feet.

"What did the Doc say, pal? What did he say?"

Larry forced a grin. "Nothing at all, Blimp. Just a derangement of the disks of the fibrocartilage between the condyles of the femur and the head of the tibia."

Blimp turned a scared face toward Willie. "It sounds fatal," he gulped.

"A sprain," Larry said.

"Doctors!" Blimp sighed. "They give you a diagnosis and prognosis of a hangnail and make you think you've only got twenty-four hours to live, just because they can't put things in simple English. I'm glad you explained, Larry. Willie hasn't the education we have."

"Tough," Willie sympathized. "You don't get to dance with the pretty mice next Wednesday night, Larry. And Maureen is going to be there."

"It's an ill wind that doesn't blow even me some good," Blimp philosophized. "Now, if only a couple of other junior Gregory Pecks and Van Johnsons can manage to pick up something contagious I will have quite a time for myself."

"Come on," Willie said, nodding at Blimp. "Help me get the casualty home."

The commencement exercises were held in the historic brick church just off the campus. The June day was perfect, warm enough to allow windows to be opened and to admit the whispering rustle of the trees and the songs of the birds. Dr. Farrington delivered the address.

"Every year at this time," he said in closing, "I remind the boys that are leaving of a certain rule we should all follow if we ever want everlasting peace and understanding. It is almost new, yet older than these surrounding hills — new because it has hardly ever been used. That rule is the Golden Rule."

A peaceful silence filled the church.

Blimp took a handkerchief from his pocket and Larry quickly caught him by the wrist. "No."

"It is only to take something out of my eye," Blimp whispered.

A line of boys filed to the platform, received their diplomas, and passed out into the bright sun.

Tom Barstock said, "Nice going, boy," and put an arm around his son.

"How's that knee?" And Larry was in his mother's arms and she was crying.

"O mother," Susan said, "this isn't anything to get sad about. You'd think Larry was getting married."

"Well, well, if it isn't the belle of Springvale, Connecticut!" a voice boomed.

"Blimp!" Susan cried, and held out her hands.

"Your one and only big moment," said Blimp. And then: "Dad, this is Mr. Barstock, Larry's dad. Mr. Barstock —"

Willie Gaverstein came up, fairly dragging a little short man wearing thick eyeglasses. "My pop, Larry," Willie said proudly. "Did you ever see so many fathers and mothers?"

The Crockers, the Barstocks, and the Gaversteins went to the Westbrook Inn, and soon Tom Barstock and Willie's father were telling each other how they'd straighten out the world if given half a chance, and Mr. F. T. Crocker, of Minnesota, was reminding them that they might have had something to do with creating the mess.

"Yes, yes," Mr. Gaverstein said. "That is so. Never be critical of a cure unless you can supply the patient with a better one."

60

"How come you turned out as you did with such a brainy father, Willie?" Blimp asked.

"The unions," Blimp's father said, "are destroying the good foundation they built. The oppressed, more often than not, use the evils they rebelled against when they find themselves in the driver's seat."

"Oh, brother," Willie groaned. "We must put a stop to this."

"Mind if we leave you for a while?" Larry asked his mother. "We want to show Susan around."

"Yeah," Blimp said loftily. "The trophies I won at Westbrook. I want her to carve her initials in a tree. All that stuff."

"Run along," Solomon Gaverstein said. "We will sit here and brag about you."

As the young group left the inn, Tom Barstock said: "They feel very old. They don't realize how young they really are."

Later came the packing and the good-bys. Larry parted from Willie on the station platform and was not ashamed of the mist in his eyes.

Blimp pounded him on the back. "See you at Kenton, pal. Don't let Susan marry any of those counts or dukes until she checks with me. Willie, write me. You know, in Minnesota, by the waters of the Minnetonka." Blimp kept talking fast.

Sitting by a window as the train pulled out, Larry craned his neck for a last look at Westbrook. Year after year, the old trees would don fresh, spring foliage. Their rustling, Larry thought, might be the whispered voices of all the students who had ever gone to the old school. He looked back until there was nothing more of the town to see.

For weeks after he came home for the summer, Larry missed Blimp Crocker and Willie Gaverstein. He could see Blimp crouched over the ball and could hear Willie calling signals and see him banging the rumps of his linemen with the flat of his hand. When Susan finally got away to summer camp, loneliness swept in and over him. He was impatient to get to work at the lumberyard, but he had to wait awhile longer until he was sure his knee was strong enough.

Downtown, late one afternoon, he ran into three friends, Sammy Doherty, Eddie North, and Harry Fielding. They rushed him along with them to a drugstore for cokes with a dash of orange.

"You were gypped," Sammy said. "Wardell never saw those papers, I guess, that said you were headman at Westbrook."

Larry changed the subject. "Whatever became of that little blonde girl? The one who thought she looked like Lana Turner? Ethel somebody or other."

"Gritzmyer," Eddie North said, and made a wry face. "She moved away. If I were you I'd go to Vail and show Wardell. I'd stomp all over that Gorcey guy."

"What's at the movies?" Larry asked, finishing his second coke.

"A picture starring that guy who used to play with the

Dead-end Kids," Sammy said. " He's on a radio program now. Leo — Leo Gorcey."

Larry laughed. " Let's go somewhere else."

The summer passed quickly. The work at the lumberyard was rugged, but a good test for the knee Larry had twisted. Twice, after he'd felt slight twinges, he'd gone to see the family doctor.

" These injuries are tricky," the man had said. " Sometimes it takes a year or more for them to definitely heal. I wouldn't put too much strain on that knee if I were you."

On week ends, Larry went down to Compo Beach where Eddie North's folks had a cottage. He and Eddie threw a football around and trotted up and down the beach to build up their wind. Specialty men, particularly kickers and passers, Hunk McQuade had often said in his book, should practice during the summer months, for there is not sufficient time to fully develop during the regular season. Larry baked the troublesome knee in the hot sun for hours at a time and, when September came around, felt fit. The scales said he had put on nearly ten pounds. His skin was deeply tanned.

" Look at him," Tom Barstock said to his wife. " Nearly six foot tall and one hundred and sixty-eight pounds. By the time he's a sophomore he'll hit one hundred and eighty. Quite a hunk of offspring, isn't he? "

" I like my men plump," Susan said, peering over the top of the book she was reading. " What did Blimp say in the letter you got from him last week, Larry? "

" He asked how was the little twerp and if you were true to him," Larry said. " I don't think you've got a chance against those corn-fed gals out in Minnesota."

" Wait until I see that fickle character," Susan said, unperturbed.

" Susan! " Mrs. Barstock said, shocked.

Larry followed his father into the living room. There were only a few more days of vacation and he felt he would need a bigger allowance than he'd had at Westbrook. He was steadily growing out of the clothes he owned.

"We won't worry too much at the moment about that," Tom Barstock said, when Larry brought up the subject. "Conditions at the factory are steadily growing better, and I can't see why they won't continue to improve." He took time out to set a cigar going. "You were something of a star at Westbrook, but there'll be half a hundred stars at Kenton."

"I know that, dad. The competition will be tougher than I've ever had before."

"There's something else," his father said. "It has to do with personalities, connections, and the power wielded by small cliques. They're minor hazards from a distance, but aggravating obstacles when you run into contact with them. They're in business and in every walk of life. You'll find them at Kenton. At smaller colleges they are not so difficult to ferret out and overcome."

"Campus politics?" Larry asked and nodded. "But if I keep up in my studies and show Hunk McQuade I'm good enough for his team, what's going to stop me?"

Ten days later, Larry arrived at Kenton and found Blimp at the station.

"Wait'll you really see this layout, pal," Blimp cried. "I've given it a complete going over. I saw some Pundits. Honest! They walk, and they talk, and they eat the same stuff we do. Wait until you see where we're going to hive up in Fairfax Hall. Some cell block, I'm telling you. And I saw the warden —"

"Hold it," Larry said. "You're a green freshman; you're supposed to be stunned by it all. You'll get your ears pinned back soon enough."

"Give me one of the bags," Blimp said. "How's the old knee that almost made you a housemaid? Let's grab a taxi and get parked, and then look over the campus. How is Susan?"

"You know that snapshot of you in the football suit?" Larry asked. "Well, it is on her vanity, Blimp. Right alongside a bottle of perfume called 'Reckless.'"

"How do I manage it, Larry?" Blimp purred in mock ecstasy. "The mice just seem to lose all sense of balance when I give them a little attention. He-e-ey, taxi!"

A taxi drew up to the plaform. Larry, about to toss his luggage in, was stopped by a voice that turned him around abruptly.

"Hold everything," it said. "Frosh wait until their betters are served."

Larry recognized Mel Jardin, editor of *The Kenton Opinion*.

Blimp grunted: "Oh, oh! Don't look now, Larry, but —"

"Well, if it isn't the soap-box philosopher," Jardin said. "Vince, keep an eye on him; he's something special. And meet Larry Barstock, runner-up to Chuck Gorcey, of Canford, in the Wardell sweepstakes. Put your bags in the taxi, Vince."

"Not so fast," Blimp snapped, and dropped a heavy bag on Jardin's toe.

"It's their taxi," Larry said, and took Blimp by the arm. Like all first-year men at college, he expected a good-natured pushing around, but Jardin's intentions of rubbing it in seemed obvious.

"Take the hack, pal," Blimp surrendered. "I'll take my advertisin' elsewhere when I've lost a dog."

Jardin said: "Vince, you can see that this new generation hasn't had the right bringing up. We'll have to take them in hand.

"In that case," Blimp said pointedly, "we have a right to know who's giving us our training."

Jardin's face reddened. "Vince Pask," he said, making the introduction.

"Hi!" Blimp said, and put out his hand. "I'm Walter Stymus Crocker, Junior, of Minnesota."

"It's a pleasure," Larry said quietly. Jardin and Pask drove away in the taxi, and Blimp growled: "Continued in tomorrow's paper. Don't tell me you didn't expect this from Jardin."

"I didn't," Larry said slowly. "But I can see I should have."

Stowbridge, the home of Kenton, was a picture town nestling in the Berkshires. Just beyond the eastern fringe of the campus was the Kenton Stadium, walled on one side by century-old pine trees. From the highest seats spectators could look out over a panorama that, stretching far into the rolling hills, included turquoise-blue lakes and sparkling mountain streams. Beautiful purple shadows played along the valley slopes when the sun was low.

Larry's first glimpse of Kenton's ivy-covered buildings took away his breath, and there was a trace of awe in his eyes as he stood with Blimp on the steps of Fairfax Hall. Pride quickened the beating of his heart.

"Not a bad setup, is it?" Blimp inquired, chewing on a peanut bar. "Quite a frat house across the way, Larry. Maybe Alpha Lambie Pi, huh? Let's go up and rest the old dogs, son."

The spacious room was furnished with two beds, twin dressers, a study table, and two easy chairs.

"We've got to hang up some pictures," Blimp quipped. "A few touches of chintz would make it homey."

Larry grinned his appreciation and listened to sounds building up outside. It was a Westbrook Prep first-week racket magnified a hundred times, and suddenly he knew he had never felt so uncertain and insignificant. This was Kenton

University where Hunk McQuade built his football teams. This was Kenton, and he was a part of it. The feeling was a little frightening, but at the same time good.

"We'd better hunt up the proctor and see what kind of fish he is," Blimp suggested. "I might decide to do a little cooking in my room."

The next three days were hectic with the complications of registration and orientation. The president appeared briefly, a tall, rawboned man with a Berkshire twang and stolid countenance, and welcomed them to Kenton and assured them they would get along handsomely if they adhered to Kenton tradition and Kenton standards. There was a three-hour physical examination in the infirmary, a conducted tour of the campus, and the business of deciding just which subjects to take.

Larry eagerly drank in impressions. New faces and new voices. The reluctance of certain groups to become friendly to the new crop of students. The confused babble of talk in the dining hall. The line-up at the athletic office where candidates for the freshman football team registered and secured their medical slips on the third day.

Words flowed freely from the football manager. "Glad to see you, boys. Practice starts day after tomorrow. As soon as you get your slip and your physical is O.K.'d you'll be assigned to a locker and handed a uniform. And good luck. The name? Gorcey? How do you spell it? Oh, Chuck Gorcey, from Canford Prep. Nice to have you on the team, Gorcey. Congratulations on that award."

"The cross I bear," Blimp said far back in the line. "I bet Hunk McQuade is kicking up his heels and celebrating. Where are you from, Barstock? Where did you ever play? Crocker, is it? Didn't you get in the wrong line?"

A sandy-haired freshman turned around and grinned at Larry. He held out his hand "Art Parmenter. Call me Red."

"Barstock," Larry said, and gripped the proffered hand.

67

"This oversized comic in back of me is named Crocker. Goes by the name of Blimp."

"I met both of you before," Parmenter said. "I played for St. Michael's. You two shouldn't have any trouble catching on with Widmer."

"What kind of a guy is the frosh coach?" Blimp asked.

"Tough, they tell me," the redhead said as they moved up a few feet. "Strict disciplinarian. He knocks his material into shape for Hunk McQuade, so he doesn't fool around."

"How about the big team this year?"

Parmenter didn't know. "I see the varsity was ordered out for practice a week earlier this year. Guess McQuade is thinking about last year. It was a bad one."

Gorcey came walking along the line, a slip clutched in his hand, his head held high.

"Hi, Chuck!" Blimp called. "You're looking in the pink."

"Good luck," Larry added.

"Thanks!" Gorcey stopped. "Lots of it yourself. How's that knee, Larry?"

"Plenty sound," Larry said.

Chuck said: "I hope it is. We'll get a banging around out there."

"We didn't expect they'd play pat-a-cake," Blimp retorted. "When do you go into the Pundits, officially?"

"In about six weeks. I've met a couple of dozen of them already and they're a great bunch of fellows. Herb Rossiter, Pumps Kennard, Ferdie Lansberg — great guys."

"The elite," Blimp drawled. "Come over and see us sometime when you go slumming, Chuck."

"Blimp is antisocial," Larry said. "See you out on the field."

Chuck went on his way.

"It's already affected him, Larry," Blimp said in an undertone.

"That's your imagination, Blimp."

68

"It's never fooled me much," the fat student said.

That night, while Blimp and Larry were giving their room the finishing touches, a knock sounded on the door and a tall, rangy boy stepped inside hesitantly. His skin was the color of cordovan and his teeth, bared in a friendly smile, were incredibly even and white.

Larry suddenly jumped across the room and thrust out his hand. "Bill Griffith, you old war horse!" he yelled. "Haven't seen you since I got that going over when we played Warren Harding. You're going to Kenton?"

"Sure enough," Griffith said. "My second year, Larry. I thought you looked mighty familiar to me yesterday when you passed me on the street."

"Say, how was it you weren't on the frosh team last year?" The colored student tried to change the subject, but Larry persisted. "You mean to say you didn't go out for football at all?"

"Well, I went out the first couple of weeks, but I found out I couldn't study, work at a job for four hours every day, and play football. I came to the conclusion I was at Kenton to get me an education, Larry, and so I dropped out. It is good to see you again, and lot's of luck."

"Glad you came in," Larry said. "You keep dropping around, Bill."

"I don't have much time," Griffith said lamely. He went out and shut the door softly behind him, and Larry looked at Blimp Crocker, a question in his eyes.

"Didn't you read between the lines?" Blimp said savagely. "His skin isn't white. I can just see him out there getting the freeze and the lumps from the native sons."

"You've got to get certain ideas out of your head, Blimp," Larry said uncomfortably.

"What ideas? Last fall Kenton had a line that was a sieve. There was a backfield man named Lansberg who was sup-

69

posed to be understudy for Hunk's left half, Witworth, and he played more minutes during the season than the regular. I read the papers, Larry. And I know a coach has an economic problem, too, and can't cut off his nose to spite his face. Not even McQuade."

Larry recalled words his father had spoken. "You think there's discrimination at Kenton?"

"Far be it from me," Blimp said, "to disillusion the young. I only know that Lansberg is the son of a man who owns a railroad. I know that plans for a new stadium have already been drawn up, and that Kenton will be looking for a lot of dough from old grads like Big Bill Wardell, Lansberg, and J. J. Rossiter, who owns all the big dairy outfits in northern New England."

"You might be wrong," Larry said at last.

"I hope I am wrong," Blimp said seriously. He looked over a circular he had found slipped under his door announcing that two new divisional majors were now available at Kenton — public service and community leadership. All at once his seriousness was gone, and he touched off his barbed humor. "Who wants to be a Rotarian?" he sniffed. "And I hate conventions."

It became glaringly apparent to Larry Barstock as he stood in the gym with almost a hundred candidates for the freshman team that pressure groups at Kenton maintained listening posts on and around the campus. Lew Widmer, the coach, made it clear that he had heard a full measure of campus gripes. He was a husky man with bandy legs who had starred at New Hampshire. His eyes were a cold grayish-blue and his mouth was wide and thin-lipped.

" Before we get down to serious work," Widmer said tartly, " let us understand each other. If there's any doubt in your minds that you won't get a square deal here, turn in your uniforms. I want no campus lawyers. There has been talk for the last couple of days that favoritism is being shown at Kenton. Discrimination.

" If there are good football men here who don't report for practice, we don't go out and shanghai them and dress them in uniform. You can be a football player at Kenton if you want to and have the stuff. It's not our fault if certain men haven't the stamina to come out and fight for a place, or if they find they haven't what it takes and quit. The only way we'll have a winning team is to pull together. Personal feuds mean the wrecking of essential morale, and can cause needless injuries. If there are any petty grievances, bring them to me. We'll try to straighten them out without the help of the student body, the faculty, and the alumni. Is that clear? "

Larry felt the lash in Widmer's eyes as they rested on him for a brief moment.

Gorcey chewed slowly on a stick of gum. "It is, Coach. I think I can speak for everybody here."

"I guess you can," Blimp murmured, and Widmer swung his head toward the voice.

"You," he said acidly. "You'd better be positive around here."

"Sorry," Blimp said, "I forgot I wasn't a Pundit." His bland grin left Widmer uncertain. "But if I keep my mouth shut and eat my spinach I bet I could be one."

Larry glanced at Chuck Gorcey. The jaw muscles of Wardell's choice were tight. Widmer, studying Blimp's guileless countenance, suddenly laughed. "O.K.," he said. "So we have a comedian here. It won't hurt, gentlemen, not a bit. What position do you play — er — ?"

"Crocker," Blimp said. "Running back."

There was a gale of laughter.

"Center, Coach," Blimp said when the gym became normal again.

"All right," Widmer said. "Let's get down to business." He studied a list of names. "When I call out, answer clearly and step toward the door. Adams — Ackerman — Andres — Archambault — Barringer — Bethune — "

For three days the players were put through light preliminary training. The regimen gradually became tougher and Widmer threw his backs at the charging block to improve their leg drive. The ex-New Hampshire player was a stickler for fundamentals, and for two straight afternoons concentrated on blocking. He had the candidates tumbling around in small groups, perfecting shoulder, pivot, open and shut, stationary, roll, knee, and slide blocks.

"Block and tackle," Widmer kept saying. "Block and

72

tackle is most of the game. You get proficiency in both and you've got a team."

Beginning the second week, Widmer called his backfield candidates around him and turned the linemen over to his assistant coach. He demonstrated the fine art of ball carrying for several minutes and finally tossed the pigskin to a heavily built player named St. Hilaire. " All right; we'll watch what you can do against second-string tacklers."

St. Hilaire hit the first man to come in contact with him with a straight arm that brought low whistles from those standing by. He ploughed through the other two by sheer weight alone. Widmer blew his whistle and shook his head.

" Your starting steps were too long," the coach pointed out. " Always start with short steps, and keep your knees high, your feet wide, and your head and eyes up and all your weight forward. You're a husky boy, but you'll meet tacklers on the frosh teams as big as you." He took the ball from St. Hilaire and handed it to Gorcey. " Show them what I mean."

Larry admitted Gorcey was a flashy runner. Widmer nodded approvingly.

" That was good," the coach said. " But all of you have some things to learn. One very important thing, always put your loose hand on the ball when you're hit, and be relaxed when you fall."

Here, Larry remembered, was something Buck had always preached.

At·the end of two weeks Widmer cut his squad and named a tentative starting team. Gorcey was at right half, St. Hilaire at fullback, and Barstock or Bethune at left half, with Sage at quarterback. The ends were Hirshmeyer and Milholland, and the tackles, Andres and Sweetser. Ollenbine and Trumble were the guards, and Blimp Crocker and Felch, the centers.

" Bear in mind that this team can change overnight," Wid-

73

mer said. "Don't think you've clinched those positions. I'll know more about you after the opener with Vermont frosh." He walked over to a table and watched the trainer work on Sage's shoulder. He glanced at the tape wound around Ollenbine's ankle, and then sought out Larry who had limped a little coming off the field.

"How is that knee, Barstock?"

"The word gets around, doesn't it?" Blimp cut in as he peeled off his jersey.

"I was not addressing you, Crocker," Widmer snapped.

"It's not my knee," Larry said. "I pulled up with a slight Charley horse."

"See that you get a good working over," Widmer ordered. He turned and slapped a hand on Chuck Gorcey's shoulder as the back headed for the shower. "Nice going, Chuck. Keep it up."

Blimp turned his back and made a sour face.

A man came into the locker room and the talk and the banter suddenly stretched thin. He wore an old sweat shirt, baseball pants, and a baseball cap. His face was seamed and brown, and there were white patches at his temples. This was Hunk McQuade, husky and capable at sixty years of age, the head coach of football at Kenton.

Widmer hurried toward him. "Came over to see my bunch, Hunk? How do they look?"

McQuade nodded. "Adequate. I watched them from the stands awhile this afternoon. You've got yourself a nice backfield. I'd like to use one of them a week from Saturday against Maine."

"You mean Gorcey?" Lew asked.

"If he's the one at left half — the rangy kid." McQuade pointed toward Larry.

Widmer's face changed and he forced a different kind of

smile. He said: "That's Barstock. Played for Westbrook, Hunk. He and Chuck Gorcey —"

"Oh," McQuade said.

"How's the varsity shaping up?" Widmer asked, seemingly anxious to change the subject.

"Slow, Lew. Not worried too much about the line. I've got that boy you had last year. Came out a little late. Griffith, the colored boy. Has a load of stuff."

Widmer said: "With me he didn't last very long. Sort of a puzzle. A kind of mental hazard, perhaps, held him back."

"I see," McQuade said, and walked out of the locker room with the frosh coach.

Blimp said: "I'm trying to remember where I've seen McQuade before. Now I know. It was in a geography book. The Sphinx."

"He knows football players," Eddie Milholland said.

Blimp nodded emphatically and looked toward Chuck Gorcey, but the ex-prep star was over in a corner talking to Mel Jardin. Blimp nudged Larry. "The press, pal. Be careful what you say."

"I doubt very much if he'll interview me," Larry said dryly.

"Hunk McQuade didn't help you any while he was in here," Blimp said. That night, after a session with the text books, he gave a snort. "I think I'll major in psychology, Larry."

"I'll bite. Why?"

"I think I've got a flair for the stuff. Take Widmer and Chuck Gorcey. The frosh coach is sold on Chuck and is building him as the spark. Because why? Because Big Bill Wardell picked Gorcey, and Widmer thinks Chuck has to be the best of the material. You catch Widmer's face when McQuade singled you out?"

"Chuck looks good out there," Larry said, mildly impatient.

"And you don't look as good as you should. Speaking of mental hazards, you've got a sweetheart, and Gorcey knows it. It was Chuck who twisted your knee. You're like a guy who has licked a toothache, but who goes around on needles and pins because he expects it to start aching again any minute. You subconsciously favor that leg and hold back a lot of your drive. Get over it, kid."

Larry said, "Sometimes you amaze me, Blimp," and tossed a book away and went over to the washstand to splash cold water on his face. Blimp's observations, he told himself, might be sound.

The scrimmaging during the week preceding the opening game with Vermont was rugged, and it became more apparent each day that Widmer was developing Gorcey as his key back, his climax runner, his spark. Larry found himself doing the blocking for Gorcey on quite a number of the coach's set plays. The realization of what was happening was no antidote for the mental hazard he packed more times than he did the ball.

In the locker room after final practice for the game with Vermont's yearlings, Widmer dissected the play of his starting team. Every player drew his share of criticism. The coach was particularly acidly critical of his guards and tackles and refreshed their memories sharply regarding fundamentals.

"You, Ollenbine! You come in too high on the straight ahead tackle. Drop your shoulders under those of the ball carrier, and bunch yourself at the impact for an extra lunge forward. That's how a team gets within striking distance. Sweetster, watch that holding. It's a disease with you."

Blimp Crocker coughed, and Widmer gave the fat boy his attention.

"You, Crocker. I want to see more speed and more accuracy with your pass to the deep man in punt formation. Bear in mind that there's one thing that can make me madder than anything in the game — blocked kicks! If it's possible, keep that two hundred and thirty-six pounds on the balls of your feet, and not on the ball."

"Correction, please," Blimp said politely. "I now only weigh two hundred and thirty-five and a half."

Widmer ignored this. "I want the quarterbacks in my office as soon as they've showered. The rest of you are through until tomorrow. Get plenty of rest tonight."

Larry and Blimp walked slowly toward Fairfax Hall.

"See?" Blimp said abruptly. "When you haven't your mind on it, that knee doesn't bother you at all."

Larry admitted that it didn't. "What do you think of it all up to now?"

"If I told you, you'd say I'm only imagining it. Let's wait and find out for sure. Huh, Barstock, blocking back. DiMaggio pitching for the Yanks."

"They need blockers on a football team too," Larry snapped.

Vermont's freshman team, during the first quarter, betrayed a woeful lack of experience. Kenton moved to Vermont's thirty-yard line on a series of reverses from a double wing, with Chuck Gorcey carrying most of the mail and Larry Barstock doing a steady job of blocking. When one or two yards remained for a first down, Sage called on St. Hilaire, the power plunger, to pick them up. During a time out called for by wilting Vermont, Blimp dropped down on one knee close to Larry.

"Yeah, a convoy for Widmer's carrier."

"You mentioned that yesterday," Larry said.

"O.K. But remember that coming events cast their shadows before. It fell on us during a train ride, pal, and at a big dinner in the Westbrook gym."

When play was resumed, the Kenton frosh again began clicking. Sage faked to St. Hilaire coming around and then faded back and looked for Milholland, floating toward the side lines like a will-o'-the-wisp. Sage hung out a clothesline and Milholland took the ball over his shoulder and slammed to Vermont's nine-yard line before he was bumped out of bounds.

Gorcey tried to go the rest of the way on a thrust off tackle but was cut down after a puny gain of a yard and a half. St. Hilaire assumed the burden. He hit Vermont in the middle and pumped to the three, where he fumbled. Larry beat a Vermont lineman to the lazily bounding ball and covered it as if it had been a live grenade. The pigskin rested on Vermont's one-yard line. St. Hilaire bucked over for six points for Kenton frosh.

Larry limped as he took his position with the offense for the try for point. After the ball split the uprights, rocketing off his toe, Widmer took him out of play.

" The knee? " the coach asked.

" Turned my ankle a little," Larry said, and had trouble holding back words that leaped to his tongue. Widmer, if he was any judge of men, should know that fixations could hurt a player. He sat and watched Bethune carry on in his place and he knew that the dark-haired boy needed more experience. Gorcey did not scintillate so brightly now, for his interference was getting smeared. Widmer saw that too, and Larry went in again halfway through the second quarter and got the team clicking smoothly once more.

Kenton was out in front 13–0 at the half. In the dressing room, Widmer pointed out the errors the players had made. He made no mention of their good deeds, and Larry felt resentful of the coach's one-sidedness.

"Nice going out there," Widmer said to Milholland, getting around to reluctant praise at last.

Blimp said, "You looked good, Chuck."

"Pardon me," Lew Widmer said, an edge to his voice, "I'll hand out the bouquets. You've been playing a setup, an inferior high-school aggregation. Show me what you can do against Pittsfield Academy or Vail freshmen and I'll tell you how good you are. Sage, and all you other quarterbacks, when you get out there next half, mix up the plays more. You're in a rut. Let's see more passing, even if you are on your own thirty. They're specializing in an open game at Vail."

Widmer's team went out on the field again and kicked off to the Green. Chuck Gorcey began to dominate the play. A neat block by Larry shook him loose around Vermont's end midway through the third period and he romped fifty-six yards to a touchdown. Again Larry kicked the extra point and Kenton was out in front 20–0. The coach called seven of his first team to the bench and inserted eager substitutes. "Great, Chuck," he said to Gorcey. And then, as an afterthought, "You'll do, Barstock."

"Thanks!" Larry's voice was ice.

Vermont's freshmen put up a stubborn fight against Widmer's B team, but could go nowhere. The stands were unusually quiet.

Blimp said: "I wonder if the varsity's having as easy a time against Maine? That Griffith was tearing things up in practice."

"The colored boy?" a reserve guard asked from down the bench. "He won't play again for at least a week. He went to the infirmary last Thursday after a scrimmage."

Larry set his lips tight and tried to concentrate on the play Vermont was trying to touch off on their own thirty-nine-yard line.

Blimp observed: " Griff didn't last long last year, either. I was reading it in the paper last night that colored G.I. veterans might have trouble voting in a certain state."

" This is a football field," Lew Widmer snapped. " Not an open forum."

Vermont's rooters roared when a wild pass clicked to Kenton's twelve-yard line. They kept screaming while the Green slammed to the four on a pair of running plays. The Kenton first stringers tensed and looked hopefully at Widmer.

" Relax," the coach said. " Give them a score. Why show our real strength to the teams we've yet to play? "

Vermont scored the touchdown, but the try for the extra point failed. There were just three minutes to go after the kickoff, and Kenton's reserves worked the ball to their own thirty-seven. Two passes were successful, but a third was intercepted on Vermont's thirty as the gun went off.

" A good start," Widmer said, and got up off the bench.

" Last one in the gym is a rotten egg," Blimp Crocker yelped, and started running, looking like a big bear in his parka. Several minutes later, he sidled up to Larry on his way to the shower. " Besides being a philosopher, I am psychic. Chuck Gorcey was the one in here last."

" Lay off, Blimp," Larry cautioned. " What you don't say will never hurt you."

Widmer called out, " Crocker! "

" Yes, Coach."

" You certainly can't help being seen," Widmer said, stringing his words out, " but you can arrange it so's you can't be heard! "

In the shower, Blimp mumbled, " What big ears you have, gran'ma! "

The first issue of *The Kenton Opinion* reached the students on the Wednesday following the frosh's second game on the schedule. They had managed to eke out a 12–7 victory over a strong Pittsfield Academy team, and the touchdowns had been largely fashioned by the efforts of Chuck Gorcey and Larry Barstock. On the same afternoon, Hunk McQuade's varsity had been scared by Rhode Island, a team they had figured to steam-roll by at least four touchdowns.

Blimp brought the college paper into his room after classes. Fifteen minutes later, when Larry and Eddie Milholland walked in, he heaved a pillow against the wall and slammed the newspaper to the floor.

"What —" Larry began.

"You haven't seen it, pal?" Blimp roared, his face fiery red. "Here! Take a look on the editorial page. Read that stint of Jardin's labeled ' Out of the Mouths of Babes! '"

Larry turned to page six. He read aloud:

" ' *A crusader has come to Kenton who presumes to question the fairness of the men coaching our football teams. Apparently the runner-up position does not appeal to this ex-prep-school hero.*

" ' *This brash freshman has started out on the wrong foot and needs to be taken in hand by his elders before he establishes a dangerous minority. We are well aware that the freshman does not hold the Pundits in high esteem, and we venture to say that he does not aspire to become a member of that fraternity.*

"'Our rebel has a mouthpiece who does not take the precaution to keep his bearish growl at a minimum while expounding his warped views. We suggest that both students make an appointment to discuss Kenton fellowship and tradition with the president of the Pundits.'"

Larry crumpled the paper into a ball. All at once Blimp saw the storm in his roommate's eyes and held his tongue.

Larry said, "Where do I find Jardin?" and started for the door.

Blimp got in his way. "I know how you feel, pal. Usually you hold me in check, but this is my day to hold you down. Take it easy. It won't do any good to punch Jardin in the nose. Anyway, I'm reserving that right."

Eddie Milholland said: "I heard they ganged up on Griffith. Three or four of the scrubs were talking it over at breakfast the next morning. Look at the big team's record so far. Why is Ben Price sitting on the bench? He's the best tackle ever to come out of New England. Why —"

"Stop talking, Eddie," Larry said. "Think all you want, but don't talk. This just about puts the skids under me. The power of the press; paper bullets right through the old ticker. I can see Mel Jardin ten years from now. I can see the stuff he'll write, maneuvering people into misunderstandings and creating class consciousness. You can fight for fair play and equal rights, and a guy like Jardin will take out the smear brush and make you a dead pigeon. I don't like cliques and so I'm a rebel. I want everybody to have an equal chance and so I'm no good for Kenton."

"Calm down," Blimp said. "If they don't want us to play

82

football, that's all right. They can't stop us from reading the books."

"Politics," Eddie sniffed. "My father said once they were the curse of the universe because you couldn't keep them from getting out of hand."

"I never resented Chuck's getting picked by Wardell," Larry said. "Some of my friends started griping, so the idea went around that I was griping too."

Blimp sighed deeply. "When are we going to report to the big medicine man of the Pundits?"

"When they drag us there," Larry snapped.

"At last you talk my language," Blimp yelped, at ease again. "I never liked you more than I do right now, pal. Your mouthpiece, yet. I should keep my voice down. Remind me to from now on, will you, guys?"

Twenty-four hours later Larry found a typed message under his door asking him to report to the dean of freshmen on Thursday, between three and four o'clock in the afternoon. That would be tomorrow. He thrust the typed page into his pocket, looked at his watch and knew he would have to hurry to get to the field.

Widmer eyed him askance as he came into the locker room. Voices lowered as he peeled off to get into his uniform. A few of the players spoke to him and he catalogued them in his mind for future reference — Eddie Milholland, Ollenbine, Andres, and St. Hilaire. The atmosphere was significantly cold, and he knew he had more than a knee to worry him through the rest of the season. His play suffered that afternoon and Widmer rode him hard, finally taking him off the first squad and letting him sweat it out with the scrubs. Chuck Gorcey evinced a definite lift as he galloped high, wide, and handsome through his paces.

When the players flocked into the locker room, Larry threw

a bombshell. In front of the entire frosh squad, he said: "Wid-mer, I want you to answer me a question, yes or no. No hedg-ing!"

The coach spun around, his mouth half open. Blimp's breath wheezed in and held.

Widmer said, "Fire away."

"That stuff in *The Kenton Opinion* — do you believe it's true?"

Widmer, his lips pressed tight together, stared uncertainly at his player for fully a minute. "You asked me to be frank. I do."

"That makes everything clear to me," Larry said. "I'm turning in my suit. I don't need football to graduate from any college. I've come to realize that a man can't go far here if he isn't in the right circle or hasn't the right friends."

Gorcey, a little red in the face, went over to the drinking fountain.

Widmer said: "O.K., if that's the way you want it. Turn in your key." He looked at Blimp Crocker. "How about you?"

"I've got too big a mouth to play football here," Blimp said. "First thing you know, I'll get a football caught in it and choke to death. You ought to have a wow of a team now you've got rid of the guys boring from within."

"We'll try and struggle through," the coach said dryly. And then, abruptly, his voice broke with anger. "Both of you clear out of here as fast as you can! If you weren't just kids —"

"Don't let that stop you," Larry invited.

Blimp and big Johnny St. Hilaire got between him and the coach.

After a moment, Larry said, "I'm sorry I lost my temper, Widmer."

Later, trudging toward Fairfax Hall, he realized that the

tempest in the teapot on the train from Westbrook to Springvale not quite a year ago had broken loose and had become
a violent storm.

"We'll try next year," Blimp said, "with Hunk McQuade."

"That's next year, Blimp. I've got to think up what I'm
going to say to Dean Murchison tomorrow."

"I want to see Gorcey against Vail frosh with Bethune or
Isbell blocking," said Blimp.

"Chuck might surprise you," Larry told him.

Dean Murchison was a bulky man with bushy eyebrows
and a mouth that always seemed to be pursed. He said, "Sit
down, Barstock," and picked up a copy of *The Kenton Opinion*, scanned a few lines of Jardin's editorial and laid the paper aside. "Tell me, what this is all about."

"It goes back," Larry said. "I was on my way home from
Westbrook last year for the holidays when I met Jardin and
Herb Rossiter. Crocker was with me. They threw their weight
around a little. We weren't awed, and Jardin as much as said
we'd hear from them when we got to Kenton. There's not a
bit of truth in what he says in his editorial."

"You and Crocker dropped out of the freshman football
squad yesterday afternoon, didn't you?"

"Let me make one thing clear," Larry said. "I do not
intend to kowtow to anyone in this world. The day of goose-
stepping when somebody blows a whistle is over. I consider
this business of fawning to a select few an unhealthy situation in view of what's happened in the world. One thing Jardin said is true. I do not aspire to the Pundits; at least not
until I'm sure they're what they profess to be. It doesn't take
a person long to make certain observations, Mr. Murchison."

"Such as what, Barstock?"

"For one thing, Wayne's Private Tutoring School. Every
Pundit on the football teams can avail himself of that service

at no cost to him. No ordinary student can take advantage of that school."

"I've heard there's such a school," Murchison said after a short silence.

"I know of at least four potential football stars who have been sidetracked, one way or another. It's common knowledge they got Bill Griffith deliberately. There's Price, who sits on the bench and watches an inferior tackle play where he should be playing. How about the Kenton varsity record for the last three years? To be brief, Sir, that is what it's all about."

"Son," Dean Murchison said, after a long silence, "you are young and have much to learn. I would say you were a nonconformist. There are discrepancies in all walks of life. We know they exist, but we choose to ignore them for obvious reasons. Nothing can be perfect and we must set our own course and do the best we can. There's a saying — 'If you can't lick them, join them.'"

Larry shook his head. "We've been willing to accept discrepancies too long. It isn't the way I want it. Fairness isn't too much to ask, is it? I want the son of a millionaire and a poor farmer's son, or a colored boy, to have the same advantages at Kenton. If that isn't possible, then the system is wrong. If the football teams, fraternities, and all other activities outside the classrooms are for one privileged group alone, then I'll stick to my studies here, Mr. Murchison, and forget what goes on around me."

Dean Murchison got up and went to the window and looked out over the campus. He said over his shoulder: "Barstock, you're a refreshing change. I've often wondered when a boy like you would appear at this university. You have my word that I'll hold everything you've said in strict confidence. I believe you to be sincere, but remember the Dutch boy with his finger in the dike. It is hard to teach an old dog new tricks.

Kenton is almost a hundred years old. It has its economic problems and they justify some of the discrepancies you mentioned." The man turned from the window. "Drop in again at any time."

"Thank you," Larry said. He went out of the office, along a corridor, and down the steps to the street where Blimp was waiting.

"Where do we go from here?" Blimp asked.

"I found out something from the dean," Larry said, as he walked along under the ancient trees of Kenton. "Big men will admit sometimes that they're wrong."

"I never liked riddles," Blimp growled.

They crossed a triangle toward Fairfax Hall. Mel Jardin, Herb Rossiter, and a student whose name they did not know walked briskly toward them.

Rossiter called out, "Just a minute."

Larry stopped.

"You were requested to call on the president of the Pundits," Jardin said.

"My appointment book has been crowded lately," Blimp said sweetly. "Let me look in it and see if — "

"Do we take them, Mel?" the unknown student demanded.

Larry's lips thinned. "I stopped playing kids' games long ago, Mister."

Rossiter lunged at Blimp. Larry thrust out his foot and the varsity player fell headlong into a privet hedge. Blimp lowered his head and struck the unknown Pundit in the middle and let out all the boy's breath. Jardin hung back.

Eddie Milholland and big St. Hilaire came out of Fairfax Hall. "Save one for me, Larry!" the frosh fullback cried.

The fight was over.

Rossiter brushed dried privet leaves from his trousers. "You've asked for it now, Barstock," he said in anger. "You won't last two years at Kenton." He walked rapidly away and was followed by Jardin and the third boy who was still trying to get back his breath.

" Is this the way you worked on Bill Griffith? " Blimp called after the Pundits. He went up the steps of Fairfax. " My big mouth! " he chortled, well-pleased with himself. " But what fun I get out of it! "

Larry and Blimp found themselves in a world apart. Students who were secretly elated over the humiliation of Jardin and his friends gave them little more than a nod in passing lest they be included in the reprisals they felt sure were coming. For to be counted friendly to the so-called rebels might hurt their chances of being pledged for Kenton's fraternities and leave Commons their only social refuge.

"Well," Blimp said, looking up from a book, "unless the faculty takes orders from the Pundits — which I doubt — we ought to make the dean's list. We'll soak in the knowledge. No distractions at all. We'll just live like hermits and plug for the marks."

"If we don't want to play football for Widmer," Larry said, "that's our privilege. They can't fire us out of Kenton for refusing to be pushed around. If highhandedness is a Kenton tradition, you can have it, Blimp."

"We're not loused up as much as you think, pal. A lot of guys are just aching to break down and ask us to cut them in on this deal. Give the thing time."

Larry and Blimp came back from a movie the following Saturday and found Johnny St. Hilaire sitting on Blimp's bed. The fullback looked beaten physically and spiritually. There was a bruise on his right cheek and his wrist was taped.

"Don't let the Gestapo find you in this hide-out," Blimp warned. "How did the frosh do it at Providence?"

"We got licked," St. Hilaire said tightly. "Remember what Widmer said about blocked kicks, how he hated them? The Brown frosh blocked a punt in the last quarter. Blimp, they sure miss you on that team."

"Nuts," Blimp said, and dumped half the contents of a sack of salted peanuts into his mouth.

"And Gorcey misses you, Larry. Without a good blocking back, he's no better than the average. Now Widmer can find a fullback to take my place. He pulled me out in the third period and told me what he thought of me. I gave him plenty in return. He's been on me hard because I've been friendly toward you guys."

"Hunk McQuade's team was taken by Manhattan this afternoon 7–6," Blimp said. "It looks like another steam roller for Vail."

"Jardin and Widmer can place the blame right here in our laps," Larry pointed out, "if they're pressed hard enough. They can say I deliberately set out to make Wardell's choice look bad and that I'm handing it back to Big Bill for picking Gorcey."

"They won't get away with it," St. Hilaire said. "I know how a lot of the boys feel. They're with you, Larry. It's taking them a little while to make up their minds to throw off the spell that the Pundits have woven around this campus for the last few years."

"Tell them to hurry," Blimp implored. "We're hanging on the ropes and we want to play football next year."

St. Hilaire stood up. "I dropped in to let you know how I stood."

"Thanks for coming, Johnny," Larry said. After the fullback was gone, he sat at the study table and stared at the wall. He had never wanted any of this disruption. He could not remember ever meeting a single person he'd actually disliked before coming to Kenton. He searched his conscience

90

and knew he could live with it, come what may. He wondered what his father's reactions had been to the last letter he'd written home.

Blimp said: "I'm hitting the sack. If you happen to be communing with any of the muses, be sure it is Clio — she knows her history. Ask her will she tutor me and how much she'll charge?"

Larry rose up out of the doldrums and grinned. "I don't know what I'd do if you got booted out, Blimp."

Late the next afternoon Larry found a letter on his cot and he suddenly remembered the scrawls on a blackboard in the gym back at Westbrook Prep.

The letter was like Buck Frazee, straight to the point.

"It certainly was a shock to me to hear you'd quit the freshman team. I know you must believe you have a good reason. I read that first issue of The Kenton Opinion. *You have been handed a bad break at the beginning, and no doubt this big time football is a trifle disillusioning.*

"Lew Widmer knows his football, Larry, but I've heard from reliable sources that he isn't such a good judge of men. Personalities to him look as much alike as apples in a barrel. I still believe you'll work things out and get a solid footing, and that next year I'll read about you and Gorcey and Blimp tearing up Vail. The best of luck to you. How is Blimp?"

Larry read the letter again and a blur garbled most of the scrawled words. Here was a touch of Westbrook. Here was a part of Buck. Abruptly a lot of the heaviness left him and he felt his courage lift. He suddenly recalled something he had learned in his senior year at prep: When Mrs. Browning asked Charles Kingsley the secret of his successful life, he had replied, "I had a friend."

Blimp Crocker came in growling and slammed a book on

the study table. "It happened for the third time, Larry. I went to Nick's for a couple of scoops of ice cream. There were four or five guys there, but Nick told me his supply was almost gone and he couldn't serve more until tomorrow. You know what I think?"

Larry nodded and handed Blimp a slip of paper. "I found this on my bed when I turned the counterpane down."

Blimp read aloud, "'You are not wanted at Kenton.'" He crumpled the note to a pellet. "I found one under my plate at dinner. The war of nerves, huh?"

"There's a letter from Buck on the table. Read it, and you'll feel better."

"Buck?" Blimp pounced on the letter. Before he read it, he said: "There's a Boston sports writer here. He's been prowling around the campus and Mel Jardin is trying to keep close to his coattails. Wonder what he's here for?"

"I can make a guess," Larry said.

At nine o'clock knuckles rapped softly on the door of the room. The man who came in was Ray Conahan of *The Boston Courier*, whose face had smiled at readers of his column for almost a decade.

"Barstock?" Conahan inquired, and Blimp excused himself and left the room at once, turning at the door to give Larry a signal.

"Right," Larry said. "Nice to meet you. I've read your stuff for a long time."

"Thanks." The writer sat down. "You have sort of upset the apple wagon, haven't you? My business is to get the facts. There have been rumors going around —"

Larry shunted the subject aside and kept watching the clock on the shelf over Blimp's cot and the door. Conahan became affable. He sympathized with Larry's stand against Widmer and referred slightingly to the Pundits. It was his candid opinion that new brooms were sorely needed at Ken-

92

ton. He was talking persuasively when the door opened and Blimp came back. With him were two other students — and Hunk McQuade.

"Now I'll talk to you, Mr. Conahan," said Larry. "You know Mr. McQuade. The others are George Kyle, who works for Mel Jardin on the college paper, and Vic LeMore, proctor here at Fairfax Hall. If there are differences here at Kenton we'll settle them within the limits of the campus, and not with the help of Boston sports writers. I have nothing to say. If Mr. McQuade wants to make a statement, all well and good. However, if he had one, you'd probably have had it from him hours ago."

"You're wasting your time, Ray," Hunk McQuade said, and studied Larry's face. Blimp thought the varsity coach seemed uneasy, and just a trifle uncertain.

"Mr. Kyle is a Pundit," Larry disclosed. "Perhaps he has a statement to make."

"The *Opinion* will appear on Wednesday," Kyle said nervously. "If there's anything in it of interest to your readers, we'll give your paper the permission to use it, Mr. Conahan."

"I can get a train out at ten-fifteen," the columnist said with a wry smile. "One thing I found out, Barstock. I don't believe you're the real troublemaker here. Thanks for the buggy ride, and good luck against State and Vail, Hunk. You get a lot of what's going on by reading between the lines, and from what people don't say. Good night."

Conahan shut the door softly behind him. Kyle and LeMore departed a few moments later, and Hunk McQuade sat down in Blimp's easy chair as if he'd suddenly become weary.

Blimp picked up a banjo, plucked the strings once or twice, then tossed it aside.

"I'm grateful for the way you handled Conahan," Hunk said. "All we need is tub-thumping in the big newspapers to get the alumni on our necks. We can't always have winning teams. There are injuries, lack of the right material, and circumstances over which we have no control. If there is dissension here, as you say, we'll lick it without help from outside. I'm reserving judgment in your case and in Crocker's. The frosh team needed you badly, but you walked out. To play on my team —" McQuade gestured impatiently as if he was not quite sure of his own observations.

"The frosh team doesn't need us as badly as we need our self-respect," Larry said.

McQuade got up. "Next time, send that sports writer directly to me."

"Yes, Sir," Blimp said, and swallowed hard.

Larry wondered if there were two sides to the varsity coach and if Hunk McQuade, like Dean Murchison, did not inwardly resent being reminded of discrepancies that had long been ignored. "They can't put words in our mouths this time, Blimp," he said, after McQuade had left.

"What a politician you'd make," Blimp said. "I smelled Kyle burning. I can't wait until we report for the big squad next year. It should be quite a team. You and Gorcey, and Griffith and me —"

"Go ahead and dream, Blimp," Larry said, and peeled off his sweat shirt. "Still — it could be."

Larry and Blimp sat together in the crowded Kenton Stadium when Hunk McQuade sent his varsity team out against State. The Maroon had won but two out of five, and State smelled the first victory over Kenton in seven years. Its team was light, but fast, and was always a threat through the air within fifty yards of an enemy end zone.

"Same backfield," Blimp said, high up in the stands on the thirty-yard line. "Rossiter, Lansberg, Dekker, and Cope. Is Price in at tackle?"

94

Larry shook his head. "It's number 37, Huffine."

The whistle blew and the Maroon swarmed up the field to meet State's opening thrust. A fast man had picked up the ball on his thirteen and was angling like a frightened hare toward the east side of the field. He reversed, knifed through three Kenton tacklers and was not flattened until he reached his thirty-six. The crowd settled into their seats and waited for State's first play from the T formation. The play was deceptive and caught Kenton flat-footed, a quick kick that sailed over Rossiter's head. The pigskin bounced tantalizingly toward Kenton's nine-yard line, to roll out finally on the three.

"Smart," Larry said, and clenched his fists. The Maroon defense dug in, Lansberg back in his end zone, his arms outstretched. The ball came to him from the pivot man a trifle low and he had to hurry his kick. State surged forward and a big guard threw himself at the ball and bounced it off his body. There was a crazy scramble, and a massed groan came out of the stands. When it was cleared, a Kenton player was smothering the ball and State had two points.

"Just like that," Blimp ground out. "Now we'll see a football game."

Stung, Hunk McQuade's big eleven took the offensive after State's kickoff traveled but twenty-one yards. Rossiter got six yards on a cross buck. Cope lost a yard on a smash inside State's left tackle. Lansberg dropped back and kicked to State's safety man on the visitors' twenty-four. It was the State scatback again putting on his specialty of running back punts, and he squirmed and twisted to his thirty-two. But there Kenton held and State had to get the ball away.

Kenton got nine in three tries, and the quarterback then wisely called for a kick. State's forward wall came tearing in, but Lansberg booted the ball clear. It became glaringly apparent to Larry and Blimp that State was an inspired team, keyed up for this game, and functioning with a precision that told of singleness of purpose and strict adherence to each man's assignment. The Kenton eleven looked uncertain and jittery and, three minutes before the half, blew their best scoring chance inside State's fifteen by fumbling on third down with but three yards to go.

Hunk McQuade took Lansberg and Dekker out and replaced them with Witworth and Pumps Kennard. He put Vince Pask in at tackle in place of Huffine, and Blimp sniffed his displeasure.

" Price glued to the bench, pal. What's he got, a fractured skull? "

State booted out of danger and trotted off the field at the half with a 2–0 lead. Blimp snapped on his portable radio and tuned in on the Vail-Halvard game. The half at Boston had not run out.

". . . number 82 made the tackle. Vail asks for time out. Looks like Gorman is hurt — but not badly. Vail leads 10–0 and they're now on Halvard's twenty-two. Less than a minute to go. They line up again, and it looks from here as though they'll pass. Nacelli is fading back, he's looking for a receiver. He fires and — the ball is batted down by — "

" Turn that off! " a Kenton supporter shouted at Blimp.

" Your father's mustache," Blimp countered. " Can't you take it? "

" It's one of the rebels," a voice said.

" Turn it off," Larry said. " I don't like it either, Blimp."

Blimp was aggrieved. " Want Crosby or Dinah Shore? "

When play was resumed, Lansberg was back in. Pask was still at right tackle.

There followed a tussle that would not soon be forgotten at Kenton. The Maroon got a break in the dying moments of the third period when they intercepted a State pass on their own thirty-one. Huffine carried it back to State's forty-two

96

before he was run out of bounds, and for the first time, the Kenton cheering section put some heart into its work.

Two running plays gained six yards and then McQuade's quarterback took to the air. A long pass to Jackael, Kenton's lanky left end, clicked, and the Maroon was on State's eight. Cope and Lansberg smashed at the enemy line and rammed the ball across on the fourth try. The cheers forced Blimp to plug up his ears.

He said, " Vail beat State 28–0. "

Kenton's kicker put the ball through the uprights for the seventh point, and that was the game.

" Pardon me if I don't seem too delighted over this," Blimp said as he picked up his radio and headed for the nearest aisle.

"Wonder how Widmer's team made out against Vail frosh," Larry mumbled, but Blimp was not listening. He was blocking traffic in the runway, watching a player wearing the numerals five and four. The boy was Ben Price, and he seemed to be arguing with McQuade. The tackle finally tossed a helmet high into the air, and walked swiftly away.

" Come on! " the crowd yelled good-naturedly. " Get out of the way, big boy. Want us to move you? "

" Try flattery," Blimp grinned, and moved away.

That night, when Blimp and Larry crossed the campus on their way to a movie in Stowbridge, they were hailed by a group gathered on the porch of the big old-fashioned house that sheltered the members of Commons. Johnny St. Hilaire was there, and Ben Price and Red Parmenter sat beside him. " We're now beyond the pale ourselves, Larry," Johnny said, " so what can we lose being friendly? Ben quit the varsity this afternoon."

The husky farm boy nodded. " Takes a lot of a man's time for football practice, and I can't afford to give so much when all I do is sit on the bench gathering splinters. I told Hunk McQuade after the game. I told him I was going to concentrate on high marks and catch up on some sleep and chocolate cake. I've been in just seven minutes of play since the start of the season. I know I'm not that bad."

Red Parmenter said: "We got laced pretty this afternoon, Blimp. Only 20–6. Widmer was a wild man. How about coming over to Commons? The food is strictly from hunger, but look at the money you'll save to prance around with the mice."

"We'll think it over," Blimp grinned, and looked hopefully at Larry.

"We'll be over, Red," Larry said. "Let's go, Blimp, or we'll miss the second show."

Out of earshot, Blimp remarked: "The ice is broken, pal. In a few weeks we'll have a lot more lepers on our side. We might even live to graduate."

"I'm not in favor of two factions here," Larry said seriously. "I'll not go out of my way to influence anyone, and don't try any funny business yourself. If they choose to see things our way, all right."

A block from the movie theatre Larry heard his name called. He turned and saw Lew Widmer and Mel Jardin sitting in Jardin's convertible parked at the curb. Larry walked over.

"I guess you're satisfied, Barstock," Lew Widmer said bitingly. "You and your friend are having some belly laughs over the showing of the frosh team. You did a good job of wrecking the team to make Gorcey look sour, didn't you? Let me tell you something. You'll regret it the rest of your lives. You've played your last game of football."

Larry said calmly: "Go into the drugstore, Widmer, and look in a mirror and you'll see the guy that wrecked the team.

I asked you that day if you'd thrown in with Jardin. I got my answer and it was enough for me."

Blimp had come over to the car. " How much do you both want to bet we don't play football again? " he cut in. " And remember, they called me loud mouth! Well, take a look, Widmer. There's at least fifteen people crowding around us. This stuff would look nice in Conahan's column."

Jardin turned the key in the ignition and stepped on the starter.

For two weeks preceding the varsity game with Vail, the student body was fed choice morsels of gossip. The news that Larry and Blimp had left Fairfax Hall and gone over to Commons prompted another editorial from Mel Jardin. He called Larry and Blimp the leaders of a movement to promote class distinction at the university. They were, the editor charged, assailing the integrity of the football coaches simply because they had not been treated as saviors of Kenton football when they had alighted from the train at Stowbridge. The Pundit suggested that the president of the university take action against what he termed "the dangerous influence disrupting Kenton unity."

The day after the *Opinion* reached its readers, three more players left the varsity because they considered themselves mere props. Complaints against the varsity's showing began to trickle in and indignant alumni asked for an explanation. Hadn't Kenton, for the last three years, drawn its share of capable football players from the best prep schools in and outside of New England?

Connecticut State, considered a breather, held the big Maroon to a 13–7 win. Connecticut had been trampled by a 33–0 score the previous Saturday.

A New Haven football expert wrote that football at Kenton had gone formal. He mentioned players possessing great potentialities who had, for one reason or another, been smothered under the blanket of obscurity. Was it coincidence, the writer asked, that none of these players had been "sponsored" by men like Big Bill Wardell?

Mel Jardin counterattacked. Despite the pressure being applied by outside influence, he wrote Kenton would continue to discourage overemphasis on football. If beating Vail, he stated, was more important than the development of students and the building of character, then Kenton could dispense with two thirds of the faculty and tear down half of its buildings.

"You've got to admit Jardin knows a little about psychology," Blimp said in Commons. "This business of overemphasis on sports always gets the public, and the public is sixty per cent nonathletic. It's the best red herring to draw across what Jardin calls the 'calamity howler's path.'"

"I wonder why Prexy hasn't taken a hand?" Ben Price asked.

"Because he's sure this'll all fizzle out," Johnny St. Hilaire offered. "If he steps into the controversy, it becomes an issue officially. There's a lot of things he has to keep his hands off lest he get them burned."

Larry wondered if the Pundits were included in that category.

"We can still get burnt," Blimp pointed out. "I was talking to a soph just a couple of days ago who's been trying to catch on with the band. When certain guys found it out they paid him a visit and took him out to that statue of Joshua Kenton and told him to salaam fifty times. The guy didn't think that was funny and told them he wasn't having a part in ridiculing the memory of the founder of the college. He's not playing in the band!"

Ben Price nodded. "You haven't heard about the freshman last year named Ralph Kern? Vince Pask caught him coming out of a movie with a girl who was being rushed by one of the Pundits. The next night, with the temperature fifteen above zero, he was walking all over town in a Palm Beach suit with a placard around his neck saying he was Van Johnson. They'd put a red wig on his head and painted his face with freckles."

"And he was sap enough to do it?" Blimp asked.

"He wanted to play basketball," Ben said as though that explained everything.

Blimp said: "We've got to watch our steps, Larry. After the Vail game, everybody will forget football until next year, and crumbs like you and me, Ben, Johnny, and Bill Griffith will be buried under. We're marked men, pals."

"That frosh I told you about," Ben Price added, "said Gorcey was one of the bunch that put him on the spot. He seems to have caught on quickly."

"In other words," Blimp said, "you've got to let them kick you around before you can catch on right at Kenton. They can't say we didn't know how to take it at Westbrook, Larry. But they knew when to stop there, and there were no penalties involved if a guy fought against being tossed into a mill-pond or made to steal the bell in the old fire house. There was none of this intimidation and discrimination attached to the gags we pulled. There's a right and a wrong way of doing everything."

"When Blimp gets serious, I've had enough," Johnny St. Hilaire decided. "I'm going to bed."

Late the next afternoon, Larry received a letter from his father.

"If you believe you are right, stick to your guns. But you'll find that many things are not as you dreamed they were. You'll find certain idols have feet of clay. You'll realize there are people who crave just a little more power than the next

and, if they can't get it themselves, they'll attach themselves to those that can.

" I know how badly you wanted to play football and I admire your sacrifice for what you believe to be right; but bear in mind that yours is a voice that might not be heard until long after you've graduated from Kenton. My advice, Larry, is that you try to ignore those discrepancies you spoke about and stick to your books as you have been doing. It is futile to bang your head against a stone wall."

Larry felt despair at his father's approval of Dean Murchison's philosophy. He told himself that passive resistance, the inclination on the part of most men to follow the line of least resistance, had been the cause of the great upheaval all over the world. It was not until later that he read a pleasanter portion of the letter. His mother and Susan were fine, and Susan was sending him some cookies she had baked. Susan hoped Blimp would enjoy them.

" I certainly will," Blimp said. " Only I hope they aren't as burned up as I've been lately."

" I'll tell her that when I write, Blimp."

" No, no! " the fat boy said. " Can't you take a joke? "

Larry and Blimp sat with Johnny St. Hilaire and Ben Price in the Kenton Stadium, high up on the forty-yard marker and watched Vail roll over the Maroon. The stands were wrapped in gloom all through the crisp November afternoon, and the triumphant strains of Vail's big band swept out over the hills. Vail scored a touchdown two minutes after the opening kick-off. Turk Magriola, the Blue's spark plug, was shaken loose at midfield and ran the rest of the way without being touched by a Kenton tackler.

" It's going to be a sad day, Larry," Blimp sighed, a hot dog in one hand, a bag of peanuts in the other, and a Kenton pennant sticking out of the collar of his overcoat. " They look big, those Vail guys. Did you see that block they put on Rossiter? "

" Rugged," Larry said. " They work nice from the T formation."

Kenton tried to strike back from their nineteen-yard line but Rossiter and Lansberg gained but three yards in two tries. McQuade's quarterback was not risking a fumble or a blocked punt on fourth down, and called for a punt formation. Vail's right half gathered in the high spiral on his thirty-one and scampered up to the forty-eight before he was slammed down by Lansberg. Vail began their crushing offensive once more. They bucked over midfield and drove to Kenton's thirty-eight. Then they took to the air. A fan pass bewildered the Maroon defense and a Vail receiver caught the ball on Kenton's twelve. Hunk McQuade bolstered his line with the reserves he had, and then watched them get rolled back over their goal line in five plays.

Vail's booter failed to get the try for point high enough, but the score was Vail 13, Kenton 0 at the end of eight minutes of play.

" Look at Hunk," St. Hilaire said. " He looks like he wished he'd stayed in bed."

" Look at Rossiter," Blimp added, " he's coming out. These Vails play rough, Larry. Maybe it's a good thing we're pariahs."

" We'll score," Larry said.

Kenton did not score. After the gun, they left the scarred field of autumn, heavy of foot and spirit, humbled by a 39–0 defeat. Overhead the skies were leaden. The stands emptied, home-team flags drooping. Larry and his three friends sat where they were, a little stunned at the extent of the humiliation. Suddenly the Kenton band played, and their eyes brightened.

"Wait until next year!" a Kenton rooter yelled.

Blimp snatched at Larry's sleeve. "Look down there, about eight rows down. Next to the woman in the mink coat wearing the bronze chrysanthemums. It's Big Bill Wardell."

Larry thought the charter member of the Pundits looked smaller than when he'd seen him last. But then, all Kenton sympathizers looked deflated.

"Think he'll look you up?" Blimp asked.

"Why should he, He'll probably be in a hurry to get down to the dressing room and tell the Kenton team how hard they fought. I'd like to know what he really thinks."

"The Pundits will set him straight," Blimp prophesied. "What a heretic you'll be about an hour from now, Larry. Well, let's join the funeral march. Kindly omit flowers."

Several influential old grads were seen on the campus that doleful week end with members of the faculty, the coaching staff, and with the Pundits. Ben Price reported to Commons that he had spotted Wardell and Lansberg coming out of the college president's residence on Sunday afternoon.

"A lot of griping going around," Blimp said. "According to the papers some of the alumni want Hunk's scalp and a thorough house cleaning at Kenton. They can't understand why McQuade is the highest paid coach in New England, considering the teams he's produced the last three years."

"Because of the rep he built elsewhere," Johnny St. Hilaire said. "He has a year to go at Kenton and he has an invalid wife. He's sixty years old or a little over. This is probably his last coaching job. He doesn't have to worry much longer about the goose that lays the golden eggs."

"I don't get it, Johnny," Larry said.

Blimp explained: "It's a business, pal. College spirit doesn't enter into it. You get a contract and you get paid, win or lose. Hunk doesn't have to build any more. He's looking toward that little chicken farm in the country where he can retire.

Once he took pride in developing football players — like you, Larry. Now —"

Larry got up. "The air is bad in here. I think I'll go for a walk."

"Wait for me," Blimp said.

"No, I want to be alone for a while."

"You and Garbo," Blimp said. "Johnny, when he gets like this, don't argue with him."

It was cold in the gathering dusk. Larry crossed the campus, swung around the corner of the infirmary, and followed a street that paralleled the Stowbridge railroad station. A mile and a half beyond the limits of the town the pavement ended and he felt his boots crunch against frozen ridges of a dirt road that followed the contours of a shallow mountain stream. Leaves still fell lazily from the skeletonlike branches of the trees and struck softly against his cheeks. Here was the peacefulness he had to have when his thoughts needed sifting and when his conscience needed searching.

He had done well with his studies and was not concerned over midyears. But there was more to college life than poring over the books. He had lost much, he admitted to himself, because he had chosen to take issue with certain political setups at Kenton. He had championed the cause of students whose welfare needn't have been any concern of his, possibly because he had let certain things he had read sink into him too deeply.

Certain men like Dr. Farrington, Big Bill Wardell, and Buck Frazee must have meant what they'd said. It was not conceivable that they'd talk of fair play and altruism if they did not believe they were needed.

He sat on the bank of the stream and made his decision to continue the fight as best he could, fully aware of the odds against him and the possible consequences of failure. He got up to start back to town and in that instant dry sticks crackled

underfoot. He whirled quickly and saw half a dozen men rushing at him, handkerchiefs covering the lower part of their faces.

"Let's dampen him," a voice cried.

Larry swung with his right hand and connected, but the odds were too great. They buried him under and ripped off his outer clothing. During the melee, he ripped a handkerchief away and recognized Mel Jardin.

"Big, brave guys!" he forced out. "Lot's of Pundit guts. Six to one, Jardin. Weren't you taking a chance?"

"This is only the beginning," Jardin grunted. "Lift him up and toss him in."

Larry fought desperately. His feet were lifted clear of the ground and he was thrown into the stream. The iciness bit through his flesh. He splashed for shore and heard dim, derisive yells. He climbed up the bank, his teeth beginning to chatter. His clothes were where they had been flung and he quickly gathered them up. Lying next to his trousers was a little blue leather-covered notebook he knew was not his own.

He put on his clothes, trembling as the cold wind drove against his wet skin. He dropped the notebook in his coat pocket and walked as fast as he could toward Stowbridge. Halfway to town he broke into a run and the blood in his veins warmed and silenced the clicking of his teeth. It had been rough play and no mistake, he told himself grimly. A guy could have hit his head on a rock. Jardin and his friends were playing for keeps.

He kept running. When he finally shut the door behind him in his room at Commons, he was breathless and his damp hair was over his eyes.

Blimp jumped off his cot. "What's the matter, Larry? What happened?"

"Think I'll go out for track," Larry said between breaths. "Mile run, Blimp, or the swimming team." His teeth started

109

chattering again. " G-get something hot, B-Blimp. I met the
P-Pundits. They th-threw me in the d-drink. I-I'm cold."

" I knew it," Blimp yelped. " Soon as you get out of my
sight, you're in trouble. Wrap yourself up good in a blanket
and I'll see what I can heat up."

When Blimp came back with hot lemonade, Larry was
bundled in a blanket reading the little leather-bound notebook.

" They dropped this during the scuffle," Larry said. " It be-
longs to Vince Pask. Listen to this: 'Thomas K. Lightner,
regular; interested in Sock and Buskin — recommended. Har-
old Schram, regular; pledged at Alpha Tau; wants Glee
Club — recommended. William D. Meserve, Kenton Band —
not recommended.' "

Blimp handed Larry a tall glass. " Hide that book — quick.
If that guy finds out he's lost it, he'll be on his way here. Give
it to me. It goes under that loose board in the floor near the
washstand."

" It's atomic," said Larry, " the Pundit's Bikini, maybe."

Blimp lifted a floor board and the notebook disappeared.

" We won't use it this year, Blimp," Larry said. " We pull
in our necks for the rest of freshman year, and take what they
hand out without hitting back. Let them think they're in the
clear and let them build up for a fall. We're thoroughly chas-
tened and have become reconciled to Pundit rule at Kenton
University. Freshman opposition is never taken too seriously."

" Keep reminding me every once in a while, Larry," Blimp
said. " I'm impulsive. I see what you mean. Until we get on
that varsity team, we're just guessing about certain things,
huh? "

" You surprise me," Larry said grimly.

It was the beginning of another college year. Two dozen varsity football candidates, as nude as the day they were born, cluttered Dr. Frederick Cullop's suite of rooms in the northeast corner of the Kenton gymnasium. Dr. Cullop was the university physician and no student put on a football suit without his approval. Clothes were strewn everywhere and Cullop's eyes were harried.

Vince Pask, now in his last year at Kenton, called out: " Hiya, Chuck. You gained some weight. You'll start in where Cope left off, maybe? "

" I don't know," Gorcey said, a little more mature and surer of himself this year.

Mike O'Doul, the trainer, began checking another candidate. " William Griffith — six-one and a half, 188 pounds. Chest — "

Gorcey and Pask exchanged glances. Gorcey said, keeping his voice down, " Price is out for the team again."

" Be a tough year for some boys," Pask said.

Chuck lost his smile as four husky students walked in.

Gorcey said: " They're here, Vince. I didn't think they'd show up." His voice carried and St. Hilaire picked it up.

" Why not? " Johnny asked pleasantly enough.

" Is this a democracy? " Blimp asked.

" No more mental hazards, Chuck," Larry said. " This knee is as solid as a rock. I'm going to give you a run."

Wardell's choice eyed Larry with ill-concealed pique. "Too big a shot to waste time playing frosh football, weren't you? That won't sit right with Hunk McQuade."

"We'll let Hunk be the judge of that," Blimp retorted.

Mike O'Doul was busily calling off the specifications of the young athletes. "Heart, normal; lungs, normal; eyes, normal. You've got a slight discoloration on that left eyelid, Sondstrom. Looks like a sty coming; bathe it with boracic acid. Next!"

Mel Jardin, resplendent in sport coat and slacks, strode in.

Blimp was unable to control his tongue. "Better look in the little book, Larry, and see if we're due for the blackball. See if we're recommended —"

Pask's mouth snapped open and a muscle in his cheek jumped.

"What was behind that crack?" Jardin asked.

"Don't you remember?" Larry asked. "It had a blue cover, Vince."

"If you have that memo book, I'll take it," Pask said uneasily.

Larry ignored him and put out a hand to stop Bill Griffith walking by.

The colored athlete beamed. "How are you, Larry? Yeah, I'm trying once more. Hunk McQuade has lost five backfield men and I figure —"

Gorcey suddenly said, "I think I was ahead of you, Crocker."

Blimp did not think so. "You should have stayed in line. This isn't the place for a business meeting of the Pundits."

Pask snapped, "Get back there, Crocker!"

"Easy," Larry said quietly, "easy, Vince." Johnny St. Hilaire moved closer. Ben Price, the husky farmer boy from Vermont, waited in anticipation.

112

Mike O'Doul roared: " None of that stuff. And let's have a little quiet here."

" We'll settle this later in our own way," Gorcey promised.

" It should be fun," Blimp said dreamily. He got his locker key and a slip authorizing full football equipment. The man handing out the paraphernalia stared at him. " I don't believe it," he grinned.

" Everywhere I am humiliated," Blimp sighed. " I should sue my folks."

Next morning the squad, rigged for action, gathered in the Kenton gym and awaited the arrival of the head coach. They had been warned by Mike O'Doul to step softly. The sports writers had again been needling Hunk McQuade and predicting that the football famine against major opponents might easily continue.

The atmosphere was tense. Larry felt patches of cold sweat under his knees. Blimp gnawed at a thumbnail.

" I'm as nervous as a bride stood up at the church," he sighed.

Bill Griffith laughed loudly.

Hunk McQuade, wearing an old sweat shirt and baggy khaki trousers, walked in and nodded stiffly. His eyes, set in seamy patterns, swiftly surveyed the material. Larry thought the coach had aged considerably; there was a trace of weariness around his mouth.

" You're looking great, Coach," Vince Pask said. " Did you have a pleasant summer? "

" Reasonably so," McQuade said, his face remaining as hard as the statue of Joshua Kenton. " It's nice to see a lot of you again." His glance brushed Bill Griffith and Ben Price and settled for a few moments on Larry and Blimp. " I'm not going to give out with the usual exhortations. I'm just going to remind you that Kenton's stock on the football market has

113

tobogganed about as low as it can possibly go. Every position on the first team is wide open. I'll fire the first man who brings me a petty grievance or an imaginary persecution complex!"

Larry looked toward Gorcey and saw the shadow of a smile on the ex-Canford star's face.

"We start work right away. Look alive, all of you," McQuade said.

Outdoors, Hunk turned the squad over to Mike O'Doul. Mike's duties were manifold. The chore he had always reveled in was putting the hopeful candidates through preliminary conditioning. He gave them calisthenics until he could hear them grunt and groan. He gave them the laps until they begged for a respite.

"Just a bunch of softies," Mike gibed. "What is the matter, Crocker, can't you get up?"

"Better shoot me," Blimp gasped. "I can't make it to the gym."

"No? Well, you get two extra laps. Come on, jump. We'll get the suet out of your paunch, and the rust out of your joints. Hup!"

Larry gave Blimp a lift up.

Blimp puffed out as he picked up the pace, "What you think about the coach, pal?"

"Save your breath," Larry told him.

Later the squad straggled to the gym for blessed showers. Johnny St. Hilaire dropped down beside Blimp and Larry. "So far, so good?"

"This workout tells nothing," Blimp said. "No contact. Look at Griffith. He isn't even showing much of a sweat. If they only give him a chance!"

Larry said, "Well, we have the little book."

"I got muscles I never knew I had," Ben Price complained. "And I worked on the farm all summer."

After four days of conditioning, Hunk McQuade called his
114

linemen together and ordered them to dig in and push the heavy charging block around the field. He assembled his backfield candidates. "Pask, Gorcey, Kennard. Dekker, Platt, McKnight, Barstock, Griffith, St. Hilaire!"

Larry wondered if McQuade was rating them in the order named. The famous old coach, hatless and arms akimbo, appraised his backs for several moments in much the same manner that a buyer of beef would study a herd of Herefords.

"I think you know what you're supposed to have to be a backfield man," he said. "Speed, agility, and co-ordination, aggressiveness and guts. We're going to start in as if you never had a football in your hands before. Ball-handling and more ball-handling. A fumble can mean a loss of eighty yards. You lose the distance you might have kicked the ball and you add the distance your opponents may kick it after the recovery.

"We'll work on stances for defensive backs, and blocking, and running with the ball, and the right technique for interference, side-stepping, and pivoting. I want you to look alive and go to work on those bucking straps. Platt, I understand you were the best booter in Westchester County. We'll see what you can do along those lines later. Dekker, did you do any kicking during vacation?"

"I think I'm ten yards better than last year, Coach."

"Good. What did you do during the summer, Gorcey?"

"Worked in a steel mill."

McQuade seemed to smile. "All right; go to work on the straps."

A few days later the aches and pains were gone. For over a half hour every day, every player had his chance at the tackling dummy. Body blocking was stressed. Linemen kept pushing the charging block around until McQuade was satisfied with their leg drive. Small groups worked together, offensively and defensively. Passing combinations sweated

115

toward the perfection they needed. The kickers boomed the leather high into the sky and practiced lobbing them over the crossbars.

Larry knew he'd never felt better. He had observed Blimp working with the forward wall and knew that his stout friend had all that it took. St. Hilaire, during backfield practice, looked to be the power back to unbiased observers. Bill Griffith was the fastest and most elusive man on the field. He could carry the ball and he could block. He could pass and kick. Here was a powerful football machine in the making and Larry suspected Hunk McQuade knew it. If harmony prevailed, Kenton would come all the way back along the victory road.

Taking the required hour's nap on the rubber mattress after a grueling practice session, Larry rolled over on his side as an elbow nudged him. Blimp's face was close to his own.

"Tomorrow we scrimmage," Blimp whispered. "I don't like the looks in the eyes of some of those guys."

"Watch out for Griffith, Blimp. Pass the word along."

"McQuade has been too nice to us, Larry. I don't like that either."

"Give him a chance. And go back to sleep."

"The Pundits have been too tame."

"Shut up," Larry said, and rolled over.

McQuade picked his first and second teams the next afternoon.

"Right at the moment, this means nothing," he told the squad. "Every player here has a chance to be in the starting line-up against Maine. Go out there and battle for the places. Give me all you've got, but play it clean as well as hard."

Larry ran the names of the first team through his head as he walked out of the gym. Gorcey, Dekker, Kennard, and Platt in the backfield. Pask, Huffine, Brewerton, Spahn,

116

Thornhill, Wight, and Inman in the line. A team preponderously Pundit. Doubt assailed him as he trotted out to the practice field. A privileged few were scattered through the wooden stands, and three writers whose faces were familiar converged on the Kenton coach. One was Conahan.

Team number two lined up and watched McQuade. Larry was at right half, Bill Griffith at left half, and St. Hilaire was at fullback. Red Parmenter, a converted lineman, was calling the signals. Ben Price was at one tackle position, and Blimp was working over the ball. Ollenbine was in at left guard. Larry smiled thinly as he waited for the call to get going. This second team could have appropriately been dubbed "The Recalcitrants." He wished he could get in back of Hunk's eyes and read the thoughts milling there. Was this McQuade's way of showing the inadequacy of gripers?

Gorcey was like a greyhound straining at the leash. Pumps Kennard was walking around clapping his hands together and telling his backfield men to play for keeps. Larry glanced toward the colored boy. Griffith was nervous and was sliding his tongue along his lips. Little beads of sweat glistened on his dark skin.

McQuade said: "We'll play this all the way this afternoon. We'll have a kickoff. Barstock, you'll act as captain for your team. Pick your poison."

"I'll defend the west goal," Larry said, sniffing for wind direction.

The first string dug in and Dekker was set to run up on the ball. Mike O'Doul blew a whistle.

Dekker's kickoff slammed against Bill Griffith's chest and the interference formed. The colored boy drove up the middle, gathered speed, reversed his field and streaked toward a spot momentarily cleared by his blockers. Larry bounced Gorcey out of the play and piled up on the thirty-six with two varsity tackles, rolled over on his back and caught a glimpse of Griffith still moving forward. When he picked himself up, Griffith was getting out from under a swarm of tacklers near the side lines close to the forty-seven-yard marker.

Blimp slammed Larry between the angel bones. "Did he go? Did he go?"

"Watch it now," Larry said as he trotted over the sparse turf. "That stung them hard."

The first string, faces hard and tight, set themselves for the first offensive thrust.

Parmenter called the signals. The backfield shifted. It was a spinner, and Johnny St. Hilaire, after faking to the wing back and sensing that the defensive tackle had been drawn across the line, completed his spin and dove at the spot vacated by the tackle, who happened to be Vince Pask. St. Hilaire picked up his interference on the outside and was up to the first team's forty-seven before he was stopped.

Hunk McQuade stopped the play and pointed out a mistake on the part of Dekker. He said: "You should know by this time, Dekker, to employ a lower position and keep your feet on a line parallel with the line of scrimmage. You were off balance all the way and were easily wiped aside."

"Let's go!" Pask growled.

"Stop 'em!" Pumps Kennard snapped, and Gorcey glared across the line at Larry.

The first string expected Griffith to catapult toward them. Instead it was a center alley pass that caught them flat-footed — Larry to Andres, for seven more yards. St. Hilaire slammed through Huffine for a first down. Bill Griffith, warming to the action, got nineteen around left end, and Hunk McQuade called time.

"Take it back where it was," he said. "Your backfield was in motion before the ball was snapped, Barstock. Penalize yourselves five yards."

"Wha-a-a-at?" Blimp roared.

Gorcey and Pask grinned. Upset by the incident, Blimp passed into the dirt and the heavy first-string line charged like so many bullocks. Larry tried to snatch up the loose ball, but Eddie Wight bumped him off his feet and drove for the oval.

McQuade blew his whistle. "Crocker, I want my centers to be even-tempered. One little mental lapse like that one can throw a game away. Play football. Barstock, you should have recovered that ball. All right, get in there and play the game."

The avid first string lined up on the offense and from a single wing threw a cutback play at the seconds, with Chuck Gorcey carrying. The interference wreaked havoc with the untried second line and shook Chuck loose deep in the secondary. Two blockers took Bill Griffith out and they really hit the colored boy. Larry got Chuck. He had seen Griff take a bruising fall and he hit Gorcey with all he had, lifted him high and belted him down. Chuck's breath was knocked out, and Pask and Dekker came running, their eyes blazing.

119

"What's the trouble?" Larry asked quietly. "You should be even-tempered. You want us to all roll over and say 'uncle'? That wasn't a goose feather you hit Griffith with."

The Pundit backs tried the center of the underdog's forward wall and met Blimp, and decided to try through other channels. From a single and double wing they smashed to the second squad's forty-six. Bill Griffith's nose was trickling blood. Larry's head felt as if it had been worked on by pneumatic drills. Johnny St. Hilaire rested on the side lines, the mark of a cleat on the back of his right hand. Gorcey and Kennard and Dekker were not pulling a single punch.

Gorcey split through on a straight buck and Griffith met him in the tertiary and bounced him hard toward Larry who slammed Chuck down with a hard, clean tackle. The ball squirted loose and Parmenter recovered. There was a whistle, and Larry was positive it hadn't sounded before Chuck lost the ball. McQuade, however, stepped in and picked the ball up and tossed it to the first-string pivot man. "Let's see you go the rest of the way," he said to Pumps Kennard.

"Why did we lose the ball, Coach?" Larry asked. "It was a recovered fumble."

"The whistle had blown."

"Right," said Larry.

Blimp opened his mouth, as quickly closed it again. He looked over at Gorcey, shrugged, and took his position on the defensive.

On the next play three tacklers got Bill Griffith after the colored boy had been blocked out. The colored back got up slowly, shaking his head. He looked at Hunk McQuade for a long moment, then flashed his even white teeth. Larry had a firm grip on Blimp.

"Hold it, pal," Larry said. "We'll even it up. Watch for Kennard coming through and we'll belt him hard."

"I'll take Gorcey," Blimp said flatly.

120

The second string braced. It was Pumps Kennard coming in outside tackle. He broke through the forward wall and met Larry and St. Hilaire. They got him low and bounced him high. Kennard landed with a thump that could be heard outside the gates. Mike O'Doul had to come running with the first-aid kit. Chuck Gorcey made one threatening move, then stopped.

McQuade put another back in Kennard's place, picked up the pigskin and paced off fifteen yards against Larry's team for unnecessary roughness. The first string had six yards to go for a touchdown. Larry employed an eight-man line and waited. Gorcey roared in from a single wing setup and was thrown back into his own backfield. Blimp grinned and rubbed his shoulder. Kennard's replacement hit between guard and tackle and got but two yards. The first string was mad and showed it.

"Come on and play football," Blimp challenged them.

Platt faded back on the next play and threw a pass to his left end, who had streaked to the coffin corner. The pass was taken out of bounds, Larry knew, but McQuade called it a score. He looked at the coach, a question in his eyes, and kept saying, "Keep out of this, Blimp."

"Well, Barstock?" McQuade snapped.

"Nothing," Larry said. He looked at Vince Pask and Chuck Gorcey. "I must check up on that little book, guys. I imagine Ray Conahan would give plenty to have a peek at it for about an hour."

Pask's face changed. "Barstock, we forget things that happened last year."

"We don't," Larry said. "Did that soph ever catch on with the band? What was his name?"

The second stringers took a beating for another fifteen minutes. But Bill Griffith was still in there and on his feet when McQuade called time. The colored boy had broken through

121

the big line for fifty-five yards and Mike O'Doul was helping Pumps Kennard off the field. Chuck Gorcey was bushed. Ben Price had lost a tooth and was certain McQuade had seen Huffine swing from the ground. Larry and Blimp, soaked with perspiration and feeling their bruises, trudged to the locker room.

Ray Conahan called out, " Nice going, Barstock."

Hunk McQuade came in a few minutes later and all talk ceased. He said without preamble: " I asked you to play hard — but clean! Tomorrow, Barstock, take an ax out there with you. That goes for you too, Crocker. St. Hilaire, if I catch you deliberately clipping once more, you're through! Ollenbine, they hand out fifteen yards to the opposition for illegal use of the hands."

Larry's temper broke at last. He walked over to Hunk Mc-Quade. " We took it out there, and you know it. You jobbed us out of a score, and handed the first string two of them on a platter. You chose to ignore the way they worked on Griff. We can stand up and get slugged, and they can use every dirty trick known to the game. Fire me off this team. But before you do, let me make something clear. Without you officiating, I'll take my team and beat the pants off that pet crowd of yours any afternoon."

" We're behind you, pal," Blimp snapped.

Hunk McQuade's eyes were expressionless. " I was about to tie into the first string, Barstock, when you turned loose on me. Want to quit? "

" You know that I don't, Coach. All I ask is a fair deal. That's all I ever wanted at Kenton for myself and a lot of other guys. I refuse to play politics and bend my knees to favored darlings. I'm willing to bury the hatchet and meet this team all the way."

" Let's have harmony," Hunk McQuade said, and walked out of the locker room.

There was surprised silence that seemed to press against Larry's temples. The squad knew that no football player had ever talked that way to McQuade before and remained with the squad.

Larry asked, " What'll it be, Vince, harmony? "

Pask glanced around him as though he wanted to make sure of support. " If McQuade doesn't clean the squad of students who don't belong on it, we'll do it our way. If he wants the standards lowered, he'll find he's in a fight."

" I get it," Blimp said. " Rich grads like Rossiter and Lansberg and Wardell — play up to them. Kenton wants that memorial building and a new stadium, and so Pundits and sons of Pundits get first call. Your defense is overemphasis of football, huh? You play it for the sport you find in it, do you? Body and character building, is it? Conahan knows what's wrong here. He knows why Vail puts out top-flight teams year after year and why we don't."

" It's not overemphasis, Pask," Larry said. " It's because you have to have unity and the right proportion of strength in that unity. Read the names of Vail players last year. Frizzelli, Epstein, Magriola, Gantenbein, O'Hara, Jefferson, Kojac, and Smith — "

Chuck Gorcey said: " You have been trying to get me since that night in the Westbrook gym, Barstock. You're a bad loser and you know it."

" What have I lost, Chuck? I'm on this team and I'm working for my degree at Kenton. If you don't keep your sense of balance, you'll lose."

" Right," Blimp added, " because he can't shoot square."

"That's all I'll take from you," Chuck yelled, and lunged toward the half-stripped center. The Pundits made no effort to interfere. Larry caught Gorcey and spun him off his feet.

St. Hilaire pinned Chuck's arms and thrust him against a locker.

"Look at your pals, Chuck," he said. "Why don't they come to your support?"

"If anyone lets this get out," Larry said, "he's something of a heel. I'd warn Jardin, Vince. You Pundits could all be pretty swell guys if you'd try to be. You could still be important at Kenton. Why don't you try it?"

"Nuts!" Pumps Kennard said.

Blimp, the truculent one, kept his eye on Chuck Gorcey. "Don't forget that little notebook. The alumni might like to see it. Let's see — 'Johnny St. Hilaire, candidate for the frosh team; lacks the requirements — not recommended.' Remember, Vince? So they made you head of the Gestapo last year, did they?"

Vince turned his back. The group broke up. Larry and Blimp, Johnny St. Hilaire, Griffith and Ben Price walked out of the gym and up a curving walk toward the administration building.

Blimp said: "I don't figure McQuade. You think he was going to tell Pask and his crowd off for roughing it?"

Larry didn't know. "Now it's Pask and his crowd. Last year it was Lansberg and his group. Before that, Rossiter held the reins. That kind of system has to be broken up and I'll punch the first man who calls me a crusader or an agitator."

"My old man always said never to try and lick a million bucks," Price said. "What are a few punks like us against a new football field and an new building? We lose before we start."

Larry said, "I'm banking on something that can't be bought with money."

"Pollyanna," Blimp sniffed. "They should have buried all those Horatio Alger books your pa left up in the attic."

Price started humming a tune.

St. Hilaire suddenly said: "Did you ever notice that Chuck
124

never joins in Kenton songs? Last year when we played Vail frosh he started griping at the band when it started playing. We were backed up on our five-yard line and — "

"The boy has the Midas touch," Blimp growled. "Rah-rah — Gorcey! Touchdowns to put in the bank to draw interest."

"A Kenton football hero never has any trouble getting a good job, I've heard," Johnny St. Hilaire said seriously.

"Will you guys forget Gorcey?" Larry was impatient. "You forget that Wardell picked a swell kid last time — McCutcheon from Hilltop. All Pundits are not hopeless."

"They need only two bad apples to ruin the rest of the barrel," Johnny said. "Remember Hitler and Mussolini?"

Blimp grunted. "A lot of little dictators are spread all over the world. Chop them down to size and you'll have some peace in the world. Maybe I ought to tell that to the UNO."

"I'll talk to Prexy," Larry said dryly. "Maybe he'll arrange to have a delegate sent from Kenton."

"Take a walk, Gromyko," Johnny laughed.

Blimp followed Larry up the stairs of the dorm to their room. Larry opened the door and stopped short at sight of a sorry mess.

Papers and books littered the floor. The rug had been rolled back and all dresser and study table drawers had been ransacked. Clothing in the common closet had been taken from the hangers and thrown carelessly back in place again.

Blimp said tightly, "If I'd known they were coming to pay a call, I'd have baked a cake."

Larry surveyed the disorder for a few moments, then went downstairs. Eddie Milholland and Carl Hirshmyer were sitting in the big living room playing gin rummy.

"You were in charge here, Eddie, this afternoon," Larry said. "How did somebody get up to my room and turn it upside down?"

"Huh?" Eddie put his cards down. "The only guy, Larry, was a man who said he was a plumber and represented the guy who owns this shack. Did you and Blimp lose anything?"

"A plumber," Larry said slowly, and looked at Blimp who had come into the room. "I think I'll return the visit."

"Be right with you, pal," Blimp snapped, his eyes narrow. "I have to get my brass knuckles."

They went out of Commons, walked along Mohawk Street, and turned left when they reached Greenough Hall. The office of *The Kenton Opinion* was in the basement of Standish House, home of the Pundits. Larry banged the door open and kicked over a wire wastebasket that was not really in his way. A slightly built student wearing bifocals put down some galley proofs and looked inquiringly at Larry and Blimp.

"O.K., Buster," Blimp said. "Where's the big shot? The tycoon of the fourth estate? Oh, there's his office, Larry. Name on the door and everything."

"Mr. Jardin is very busy," said the spectacled boy.

"He is going to be busier," Blimp smiled.

Larry opened Jardin's door and stepped inside. The Pundit had company. Chuck Gorcey was relaxed in an old leather chair.

"What's the idea?" Jardin jumped to his feet.

"I'm looking for a plumber," Larry said.

"A plumber? Listen, I've got work to do here — "

"Of course you don't know a thing about the raid on our room," Blimp said icily. "Not a thing."

"I won't waste time, Jardin," Larry said. "You didn't find what you were looking for and you never will. Your pals tried to finish off Bill Griffith this afternoon. They weren't helping me and Blimp up either, after they'd knocked us down. Tell this to the Pundits: If that colored boy isn't in shape to play against State when that Saturday comes around, if any of us so-called riffraff happens to be deliberately knocked out of

126

play, that little book will find its way into the right hands, including Ray Conahan's. Is that clear to you?"

Gorcey got out of his chair.

Blimp said: "Take it very easy, Chuck, or I'll slap you down so hard Big Bill Wardell will feel it. There's a little notation in the little old blue-covered notebook. 'Kenneth Gorcey — candidate for the Pundits. Football, baseball — entitled to all privileges and considerations.' Now on the same page there is a brief and less favorable estimate of a guy standing not far away from me. I guess you remember it, Jardin."

Jardin seemed to be weighing his chances as he met Larry's cool gaze. Apparently he thought them none too good, and turned away abruptly.

"No resistance?" Blimp asked regretfully. "If I'd known I wouldn't get any, I wouldn't have bothered to walk over here. Chuck, even guys like Wardell make mistakes."

Gorcey stepped forward and swung. Blimp ducked under and rammed his big fist deep into Chuck's stomach and brought up his left and hooked Gorcey on the chin. The halfback reeled backward.

Larry said: "That's enough, Blimp."

"Get out of here, Barstock," Jardin shouted.

"Ah, life is good," Blimp said, kissing his right fist. "When a beautiful dream is realized —" He followed Larry through the doorway.

Two days before the opener against Maine, the Kenton squad crowded Hunk McQuade's office for blackboard drill. When the session was over the veteran coach picked up a slip of paper.

"This will be the starting eleven on Saturday afternoon," he said, and was aware of the breathlessness that came over the players. "It doesn't necessarily mean that I'll stand pat on this team, so don't be discouraged if you find yourself sitting on the bench for the next couple of weeks. Spahn and Thornhill will start at the ends. Pask and Huffine, right and left tackles respectively. Guards: Dobell and Inman. Brewerton, center. Sage, quarterback. Gorcey, right half. Dekker, left half, and Kennard, fullback. I want all quarterbacks to remain here to go over the strategic charts with me. The rest of you can go."

Larry sat stiffly in his seat.

Blimp said: "The same old pattern, pal. Let's get out where the air is clean."

Kennard, three seats away, waited until Blimp walked past. "That remark was uncalled for, Crocker," he said.

"Put it in lost and found," Blimp advised him. "Somebody might come along and claim it."

St. Hilaire and Bill Griffith looked beaten when they joined the two ex-Westbrook Prep stars.

"Sage!" Johnny said angrily. "He isn't anywhere up to

Red Parmenter. If Sage goes out, it'll be Platt taking his place. Ollenbine, Eddie Milholland, and Ben Price will sit on the bench and get calluses. For a while I was dumb enough to think Hunk wanted a real football team."

"Let's wait until we're sure he doesn't," Larry said. "Maybe we'll all get in there. That starting team might find themselves sitting it out sooner or later. Keep mum and fight it through."

"I'm sticking as long as I've got one leg under me," Bill Griffith said determinedly. But there was a shadow of doubt in his eyes.

Maine had a veteran team that was not rugged enough to upset a Kenton eleven. It was an alert, pass-crazy team, however, and it kept the Maroon on edge when it held the ball. Six minutes after the opening kickoff, Kenton recovered a Maine bobble on its own forty-nine-yard line after a Pine Tree State forward had clicked for twenty-seven yards. Sage started his team in high with a quick smash off Maine's left tackle. Chuck Gorcey carried for nine yards and the stands leaped to life. Then Chuck made it first down on Maine's thirty-six.

A lateral developing from a spinner bewildered the visitors. The play had the wing back taking the leather from the fullback and passing to the deep back who had circled the enemy flank. Dekker planted the oval down on Maine's twenty-one. The Pine Tree team asked for time out.

When play was resumed, Kennard drove in on a straight buck and crashed into his own interference. No gain. Sage tried to shake Kennard loose once more on a split buck, but the fullback was smothered just as it seemed he would cut into the Maine secondary. Two yards.

Larry thought that Dekker had slipped up on the play. He glanced toward Hunk, but the coach sat unperturbed, chewing easily on his gum. Sage faded back on the next play, his forward wall fighting to hold the Maine surge back until he could pick his receiver. Thornhill caught the pass on the three and stepped over into pay dirt, and the Maroon band crashed out a victory tune. Dekker, with plenty of time, looked bad when he missed the point after touchdown.

Maine got the kickoff on its nine and proceeded to work one of football's moth-eaten plays. The Red and Black's fleet quarterback raced for the east side of the field, and the Maroon defense shifted that way. Maine's left half, Honeyfield, cut past his quarterback, took the ball and set sail toward the opposite side line. On the thirty-five he began to tightrope and almost got away while ten thousand spectators screeched themselves hoarse. It was Kennard who got the ball carrier close to midfield.

"Now tell them the story of little Goldilocks," Blimp Crocker sniffed.

Hunk McQuade glanced at him.

Maine gambled and started firing. A pass was scrambled on Kenton's twenty-one, but the officials ruled interference. Maine's quarterback spread the Kenton defense with another pass formation and then threw a play at the line that netted six yards. Another pass was grounded. Gorcey batted the last aerial down and Kenton took over on its own fourteen. Dekker went back to kick. The pass was high, and two Maine linemen seeped through and almost nailed him before he got the kick away. It went out of bounds on the Kenton thirty-eight.

Maine's quarterback, harried by the big Maroon line when he tried to pass, was tackled back on his forty-eight-yard line. Kenton expected another pass, but a quick kick sailed over Kennard's head and rolled out of bounds on the Maroon eight.

Blimp groaned. "Somebody should tell them these things, and no kidding. That boy was the best booter in the Little Three last year."

130

Kenton moved from deep in its own territory, with Gorcey and Kennard carrying the burden of the offensive. Three yards, four yards, eight yards. They had to go against the clock for there were only two minutes left in the half. On their forty-yard line, after a long jaunt around end by Gorcey, Sage called for an air attack. Two passes moved the pigskin to Maine's forty-six. Gorcey fired one out in the flats to Thornhill and a Maine back leaped up and plucked it from the end's eager fingers. The Red and Black player sprinted along the side line to midfield before Dekker caught him from behind.

Kenton led 6–0 at the half.

Blimp squirmed on the bench in the locker room, fighting to keep words from slipping off his tongue. Larry lay back on a rubber mattress and listened to Hunk rip the Maroon's first-half play to bits.

The coach poured most of his abuse on the heads of Sage and Platt, the quarterbacks. " Forgotten that strategic map, C 30–40? When you're on that spot you're supposed to concentrate on sweeps and wide runs — plays for long gains, not the kind that risks loss of the ball. If the play fails there, you kick on third down, or even second down. Why did you try that cross buck, Platt? "

" Well, sometimes the unorthodox fools the opposition. It — "

" You stick to the maps! " Hunk ordered.

" Well," Blimp said to Larry, " there's one advantage in being Sittin' Bull. You don't get the lumps for things you don't get a chance to do wrong."

Johnny St. Hilaire asked: " Did you ever study English, Blimp? Repeat that, will you? "

Halfway through the third period, Kenton's attack was stalled on Maine's twenty-eight. It was third down with eight big yards to go.

Hunk McQuade said: " Get the kinks out of your legs, Barstock. Warm up, Ollenbine. Price, you're going in if they don't gain enough on the next play. St. Hilaire, stand by."

"Did anyone mention my name?" Blimp asked.

Hunk gave him a fleeting glance and went back to his gumchewing.

Gorcey failed to gain more than three yards on a spinner and McQuade sent the substitutes in. Chuck looked sullen as he moved off the field.

Kennard said: "The day is saved. The Merriwells have arrived." He trotted off.

Platt came in and took over for Sage. Kenton huddled. They hopped to the battle line and Platt barked the signals. The play was a reverse outside tackle. Johnny St. Hilaire took the ball and shoveled it to Larry and then went about some business of blocking. Larry hit inside Maine's defensive tackle with three linemen wiping the way clear, and churned all the way to Maine's tertiary. The safety man got him on Maine's eleven.

It was first down for the Maroon, and the stands began to roar.

Johnny slapped Larry on the back. "This is what I've been waiting to see, kid!"

St. Hilaire and Larry teamed up to smash through to Maine's three. On the bench Blimp Crocker was jumping around in delight. Gorcey and Kennard and Pask sat there digging up the dirt with their cleats.

Johnny St. Hilaire plowed to a touchdown on the next play.

McQuade, after Larry had kicked the extra point, sent Pask back and took St. Hilaire and Larry out and handed the assignments over to Bethune and a big blond back named Treadwell. Larry tried to wipe the hurt out of his eyes when he reached the bench. He looked at Hunk and at Bill Griffith, and trapped his lips together hard.

132

Bethune and Treadwell could do very little on the offensive. At the start of the final quarter, Hunk sent Gorcey and Dekker and Kennard back in. Price came out. The big farmer boy muttered his displeasure as he caught the blanket thrown at him.

Maine fought stubbornly, a moral victory in sight. Gorcey seemed on his way to setting up a score until Dekker had to be taken out with a wrenched shoulder. Bethune went in to do the blocking, and two minutes later Gorcey failed on a two-yard try that would have been a first down.

Maine punted out of danger and held the rest of the afternoon. The final score was Kenton 13, Maine 0.

"We slaughtered them," Blimp said in sarcasm as he got up from the bench.

Hunk McQuade said later: "It was a real workout and I'm satisfied we have a depth of material. We weren't anxious to roll up a score on a weak opponent."

Blimp looked up from the business of tying a shoe. Bill Griffith took a long deep breath and caught Larry's eye. The colored boy made a gesture of resignation.

"We'll correct mistakes next week," Hunk added. "Get some relaxation tonight and a good sleep, but remember, stick to the training rules."

"We had a lot of bad breaks, Coach," Gorcey said, eager for a little attention.

"They generally even up," Hunk said. "I seldom indulge in post-mortems. See you all on Monday."

Leaving the gym, Blimp said: "He's covering. We can't say he didn't put some of us in the game. That Gorcey, pal — he's a front runner. When the going is tough, he hasn't got it."

Larry refused to talk about Chuck. "One thing we've got to do is to see Griff. We can't let him quit."

That night, Larry and Blimp went over to the small house

on the edge of Stowbridge where Bill Griffith boarded with a relative. The colored boy was lolling in a hammock on the porch and grinned his pleasure when the inseparables walked up the creaky steps.

"Thought we'd drop by and chew some fat," Blimp said. "Look, there's a lot of games left, Griff. I mean — that is — I, well, we figured — "

"Don't worry about this boy," Griffith said. "Not at all."

Blimp picked up a small bit of colored paper from the porch floor, stared at it for a moment, and began twisting it with his fingers. The talk ran on — about home and what they intended to do when they graduated. The time slipped by. Larry could not remember when Blimp had taken so little part in a conversation.

"We'd better be going, Griff," he said. "I'm sure glad you're keeping your chin up."

"Mighty nice of you guys to come," the colored boy said fervently.

Walking back to the campus, Blimp handed Larry the bit of paper. "The wrapper came off that gum called Chickberry, and Griff doesn't chew gum. All right, so he has friends that do. But do they always leave them folded up into a neat square like Hunk does? You've seen his gum wrappers all over the place."

Larry spread the little wrapper out flat, crumpled it into a little ball and threw it away. "If Hunk McQuade went to see him, Blimp, the coach has had something in the back of his mind since the start of the year. I'm now sure of it."

"Maybe," Blimp said thoughtfully. "Hunk McQuade calling on a colored fellow. Huh!"

Larry lapsed into silence. For several days he had been conscious of a feeling of change at Kenton — a subtle sense of clearer atmosphere. The great buildings of the university had seemed warmer, and the doors of the fraternity houses less

134

inaccessible. It was a feeling he did not try to explain to Blimp.

" Griff might have let us in on it," the center complained as they walked into Commons. " We've always backed him up."

" He probably gave Hunk his word," Larry pointed out.

Blimp looked unconvinced.

Larry wished he knew what had taken Hunk to Griffith's house. The next evening, still preoccupied with the small mystery, he walked with Blimp to the tide mill on the Kensington Road. On the way back they met the dean of freshmen, Mr. Murchison.

" Well, well, Barstock," the dean said. " Last year you promised to pay me another visit. Oh, yes; they all say they will, but seldom ever do. Unless, of course, they continue to break the rules." He chuckled. " Do you happen to be going my way? "

" No, sir," Larry said. " I live at Commons. You still have quite a walk home, haven't you, Mr. Murchison? Why not come over and rest for a few minutes? We can make you coffee, and there's always something to eat around."

Blimp coughed nervously and hastily consulted his watch. " I'm sorry to have to run off, Larry, but I've got to get to the drugstore before it closes. Nice to have seen you, Sir."

The dean's face wore a wise smile as he accompanied Larry to Commons. Settled into an easy chair he gave the room a slow survey. " Quite cosy here. Perhaps you've been unaware of it, but I've been keeping an eye on you. Those shoes you left in my office — Remember? After you'd gone I put them on and they weren't a bad fit."

" I don't understand," Larry said, puzzled.

" I speak metaphorically, of course. I recall an editorial by our estimable Mr. Jardin a few weeks ago in which he stated that there was a dangerous minority here at Kenton."

" He generally exaggerates," Larry said.

Murchison smiled. "Jardin forgets that majorities are born of minorities." The dean leaned forward in his chair. "You still have your aspirations; don't reject them. You have an ambition; do not smother it. You must continue to back your own judgment and never turn back. In other words, Barstock, stay in there — and punch. Now I must be getting on or Mrs. Murchison will have my scalp."

Larry was still mulling over the dean's words when Blimp opened the door and peered in cautiously. "He gone, Larry?"

"Sure. What are you afraid of?"

"The less I have to do with brass hats the better I like it," Blimp said. "What did you talk about besides the way Charlie Boyer can smooch in a movie scene?"

"Things that lead me to believe that both of us have been on the right track. I'll try and make it clearer in a couple of weeks."

"I never had any doubts about myself," Blimp said modestly.

Larry picked up a book. "There's a letter from Susan on the table. Read it, but don't bother me."

Blimp, reading the letter, remained quiet for just thirty seconds. "Oh, yeah? She's been having just the most thrilling fall, has she? Looks like I'm riding for one. She's met the handsomest boy, has she? Take your letter and eat it, pal. I might have known anything you gave me willingly had a worm in it. I have trouble enough with the books and the Pundits. Now, I'm jilted. I think I will take poison."

"There is some ant exterminator in the closet here, Blimp," Larry told him.

Ray Conahan, *The Boston Courier*'s football analyst, summed up the first two weeks of the season at Kenton with characteristic terseness. Ben Price brought a copy of the newspaper to Prof. Hurlburt's math class and, after the grueling session, Larry read the sports column quickly before he went to the library to huddle with Virgil. Blimp trundled up and peered over his shoulder.

Conahan had written:

" Football at Kenton University remains as docile as it has been for the past three years. Hunk McQuade's paradoxical eleven managed to triumph over little Elon from New York State by the anemic score of 12–0 last Saturday. Maine was ' slaughtered' 13–0 the week before.

" The claim made by some Kenton supporters that most of the Maroon power has been bench-ridden the past two years seems justified in view of the fact that McQuade seems loath to give several players of unmistakable ability a chance to prove themselves, among these being a dusky fullback named Bill Griffith who reminds this correspondent of Fritz Pollard, and a ponderous center named Crocker who seems to have everything demanded of a first-class pivot man.

" McQuade's so-called starting eleven, with the exception of Chuck Gorcey, right half, lacks speed and cohesion. It functions mechanically and lacks ambition. It strikes me as

having a negative personality and little or no imagination. The football patriarch from the Midwest, possibly under pressure, seems to be stressing underemphasis at Kenton. If so, knowing McQuade as we do, the veteran coach has a heavy cross to bear.

"Rumors to the effect that all is not well at Kenton still persist."

"Huh, we finally got some billing," Blimp grunted.

"The coach won't be in such a nice mood this afternoon," Larry said slowly. "After this write-up — what?"

"You can't argue with the truth, pal," Blimp offered. "We got in there against Elon about three minutes all told, didn't we?"

"Here, give this paper back to Ben," Larry said. "I have work to do."

The coach walked into the gym that afternoon, calmly chewing on his Chickberry. Larry thought Hunk smiled a little as he passed him on the way to the flight of steps leading to his big office.

"Get out there and start working," Hunk called from the stairs. "O'Doul and Flip Embree will take over until I come out. Show them some imagination and ambition, Mike."

Kennard, Pask, and Chuck Gorcey plainly showed the effects of Conahan's blast. Others of the squad seemed a trifle deflated.

"All right, you negative personalities," Blimp yelped at St. Hilaire and Griffith, "let's go out and show how to win opposing linemen for friends and influence referees."

Surprisingly, a few of the Pundits snickered. Chuck Gorcey glared.

It was a rough-and-tumble practice session in which tempers flared. Bill Griffith was being belted hard until Larry Bar-

138

stock teamed up with Johnny St. Hilaire and knocked all the wind out of Kennard's bellows. Blimp Crocker nearly displaced half of Gorcey's bones when the back tried to come through B team's mid-section. Ben Price and big Ollenbine and Eddie Milholland forgot to be perfect gentlemen. By the time Hunk appeared, the A squad was thoroughly tamed.

The coach looked at a red gash on Blimp's fat calf, and eyed an ugly bruise on Kennard's left cheek bone. He asked Chuck about a cut over the bridge of his nose.

Nobody spoke. Then Blimp said blandly, "We just figured we had to find out if we had positive personalities, Coach."

Hunk McQuade said, "Go back to work!"

At the end of the session, after the players had showered and been doctored by the trainer, McQuade gave his regular talk. "You realize, of course, that the State game is a week earlier this year. State is as strong as ever, and the game will be the test for this team in more ways than one. I want you to ease up out there before the casualty list builds up. I don't mean that you should start playing charades during scrimmage. I think you all know what I mean."

On Friday afternoon, the sports writers came out with their prognostications. Some of them put Vail over Manhattan by two touchdowns; State over Kenton, 26–7.

Sitting on the steps of Greenough Hall, Blimp slammed down a copy of *The Springfield Argus*. "What's your guess, Larry?"

"The experts always judge by past performances," Larry said. "They're justified in putting us down as underdogs."

Johnny St. Hilaire said: "Conahan only gives State one touchdown over us. After what he wrote too."

"Maybe he's psychic," Larry suddenly grinned. "Maybe he picked up a gum wrapper the last time he was here."

St. Hilaire stared at Blimp. "What's he talking about?"

"How should I know?" Blimp parried.

Kenton's big squad arrived at North Bend, seat of State College, at eleven thirty the next morning. They lunched at the hotel and rested until game time. State's stadium was jam-packed when the Maroon players emerged from a run-way to the tune of their own band, and a storm of sound that poured out of the seats.

"They look big in those blue-and-gold jerseys," Bill Griffith said in a strained voice.

"They always do," Larry said, and took a bullet pass from Sage as he ran out onto the turf.

McQuade started the same team that had opened against Maine. Huddled on the bench, Blimp asked, "By how many touchdowns?"

"Shut up," Larry grunted, and watched Pumps Kennard point to the southern end of the stadium. The State captain shook his hand and trotted away.

Dekker gathered in the State kicker's long, low, booming drive on his eight-yard line and tried to cut past State's fleet ends. Maroon players began to tumble like ninepins, and Dekker was flattened on his eleven-yard line.

Chuck Gorcey tried out the strength of the left side of the home team's line. He found it potent, and had to be satisfied with half a yard. He glared at Dekker and Kennard before he went into the huddle. He said something that snapped Dekker's head around. Blimp nudged Larry.

A smash from a double-reverse setup got two yards. Sage, calling signals, decided on a punt. Dekker got it away. It was high and State's safety man got it on his forty-five, and came thundering upfield behind beautiful interference to Kenton's thirty-eight.

State's cheering section unleashed a wild roar of approval. "Touchdown! We wa-a-a-ant a touchdow-w-wn!"

State's ace carrier, Nick Saresi, jet-bombed through Kenton's middle for seven big yards. Saresi's partner, Fleck, rode

140

around Thornhill's position for first down on the visitor's twenty-four. Kenton asked for time out. The water boy galloped out on the field. Pask was a little wobbly, and was being walked around. Hunk McQuade sent three fresh men in to bolster up the momentarily addled forward wall. Ben Price and Blimp set their teeth and shifted nervously on the bench. Ollenbine spat into the dirt at his feet.

Kenton used a 7-1-2-1 defense formation. The ends were deployed about two yards outside the tackles. Kennard was playing almost five yards back of the core of defense.

The blue and gold attacked from the double wing. Saresi came scorching toward the Maroon wall, faked to his wing back, and then struck inside the weak side of McQuade's defensive tackle. For a moment he seemed to have been stopped, but the Kenton line gave way. Pumps Kennard finally nailed the ball carrier on the seventeen-yard line.

A center alley pass put State on Kenton's nine. An eight-man line tried to stave off a State touchdown, but Saresi and Fleck alternated to crash over for a score.

Larry's mouth was dry. The old doubts had their way with him once more as he watched State miss the try for the extra point. Now, if Hunk —

McQuade let his backfield stay in there. After the kickoff, the Maroon managed to drive to their own thirty-two, but bogged down there after Kennard slipped on an end around and was forced to punt. Close to the end of the quarter, Kenton had a scoring chance on the State forty-one, but a long pass, Sage to Spahn, was intercepted by Fleck, who tooled his way to midfield before he was smeared.

Chuck Gorcey was trying with everything he had, Larry admitted, but his blockers were pitifully inferior to the backs convoying Saresi and Fleck. Chuck, when he hit the line, found that he was most always on his own. He was taking a hammering.

Five minutes before the half, State partly blocked a punt on Kenton's thirty-two. From their thirty-nine, they began to roll once more. A spinner, a reverse outside tackle, a cross buck, a special scoring play, and a smash right through the middle, took them over the Maroon goal line for six more points.

The grumbling on the Kenton bench was no longer subdued. Johnny St. Hilaire got up and stamped around as State lined up for the point after touchdown try. Blimp said: " Give me a platter, somebody. I'll put the game on it, and garnish it with parsley and take it over to the State coach."

Larry growled: " We asked for it. We should have stayed in Stowbridge and gone to a movie."

McQuade, ignoring the thrusts, sat there and chewed his gum.

State missed the try for point again. Three minutes later they trotted off the field with the cheers of the crowd showering down upon them and their 12–0 lead.

The Maroon players dropped down disconsolately on the long low benches in the State gym locker room. Hunk McQuade came in and said to a student manager, " Get another man and stand guard outside the doors." He stood at the end of the room and swept nineteen of the bedraggled players briefly with his sharp eyes.

Blimp whispered to Larry, " Something's going to blow wide open! "

" The honeymoon's over," Hunk said without preamble, " and I'm finished catering to a bunch of spoiled darlings. I hope that most of you who started this game, the Maine and Elon games, are convinced now that you can't beat State. I certainly am. If you can't beat State, you can't beat Vail or Halvard. I'm sure Manhattan would break you to pieces. I've strung along with you as long as I intend to. I've thought of myself for three years, and have let some swell kids eat their

142

hearts out on the bench or quit the team. Here's my line-up for the second half."

Larry's heart was full and singing. Here was a man coming right out and admitting he'd been wrong. Here was the man he had only half believed in since he and Blimp had gone to see Griffith.

Pask, Gorcey, Kennard, and a dozen other players stood stiffly, shock plain in their eyes.

"Ends, Milholland and Hirshmyer. Tackles, Price and Sweetser. Guards, Ollenbine and Trumble. Center, Crocker. Fullback, Griffith. Right half, Barstock. Left half, St. Hilaire. You played that position at prep, Johnny. Show me what you can do. Parmenter will run the team."

Vince Pask threw his helmet against the wall. "You'll be through at Kenton before the Vail game, McQuade."

Hunk remained calm. "We'll see, Pask. You'll admit I've given you and your friends every chance in the world to make good. I want a winning team. You fellows haven't given me one. I'm not shoving any of you aside. You are still on the squad, but you're not all going to be starters. If you have the interest of the team at heart —"

Chuck Gorcey kicked a towel along the floor and turned his back on the coach.

"You disappoint me, Chuck," McQuade said gently.

"Forget it, Chuck," Kennard said. "Let's wait until these great, big, downtrodden supermen crawl off the field at the gun."

Larry moved over to where Bill Griffith stood. "You knew this was coming?"

"In a way," the colored back said, smiling.

Hunk McQuade was not finished. "There'll come a time when a lot of you fellows will have to make an important decision of your own. You'll have to decide between your pride and fair play. At my age, a man sometimes has to tell himself he must plan for the future, especially if he's had unexpected reverses during the good years. I've been thinking it over for a long time. It isn't a snap decision and it's without bias. I see nothing for a man who isn't honest with himself.

" The material has been here and I've not taken advantage of it. I'm gambling what little future I have left on this second-half experiment. I like every man in this room. I bear no grudges. If you are men, you'll be willing to sit by and give your support to the team that's going out to try to do what you've failed to do, and be ready to go in there and give them a rest when they need it."

Vince Pask said, a smirk on his squarish face: " Maybe you've heard of Barstock's little blue notebook, Hunk. Perhaps you want to duck out from under before it's handed over to certain persons."

" He knows nothing about that book! " Larry jumped to his feet.

" Don't be a louse, Vince," Blimp said.

" That's all from you." Pask shouldered his way along the bench. Larry and Johnny St. Hilaire reached out and stopped him.

" Let him come," Ben Price invited.

" Yes, come on in, Vince," Blimp said with relish.

Pumps Kennard pulled Pask away.

Hunk McQuade, who had ignored the flare-up, slapped the palms of his hands together. " Get out to the field. Parmenter, you've been studying those maps? "

" It's all in my head, Coach." The redhead unintentionally jostled Chuck Gorcey, and Gorcey ripped out, " Walk on your own feet, lemon head."

" Which is more than you can do when you're out there, Chuck," Parmenter countered acidly.

Larry took Parmenter by the arm. He ran through the runway just behind Bill Griffith. The colored boy was stepping high, and his white teeth flashed in the sun. He was a greyhound broken loose from the leash.

Blimp caught up with Larry as they came out to a great wave of sound. " Think we can stop 'em, pal? "

" We've got to," Larry said. " Hunk has thrown the dice and we're those dice. We'd better roll the right way for him."

" That's good," Blimp chuckled. " I must remember that. Yeah, we'll hit 'em, pal."

" Save your wind," St. Hilaire cried as he galloped past.

" Was I right about Gorcey? " Blimp kept on. " Now, maybe you'll admit I was."

" I'm not sure yet," Larry said. " After this game I'll let you know more."

Saresi of State booted into the end zone and the ball was brought out to the twenty-yard line where Hunk McQuade's brand new team put it into play. The first play was a slant with Bill Griffith packing the ball. Ben Price and Hirshmyer allowed the defensive end and tackle to cross the line, then pivot-blocked them out of the play. Griffith, flashing terrific speed, banged through with St. Hilaire and Larry blocking for him. The colored back was finally chased out of bounds three yards short of the midfield stripe and the Kenton rooters went Indian wild.

The State eleven, having anticipated an easier romp in the second half against the so-called Maroon second team, seemed slightly dazed as they lined up.

Parmenter barked the signals. On a split buck, Larry made four yards between State's guard and tackle on the left side. Kenton was in State territory.

Bill Griffith, shaken loose on the next play, started around the Blue and Gold's left end. His interference began to crumble when he was fifteen yards from the side-line stripe, but he quickly reversed his field, knifed through three State tacklers, and set sail for the State citadel. He found himself hemmed in again, pivoted, and bounced off the shoulder of a lunging State defense man. He kept on his feet, and then a Maroon blocker caught up with him and cleared a path to State's eighteen-yard line.

Blimp helped Larry up. "What a man! We thought *we* were hot football players!"

They pounded the dusky boy on the back. Larry said, "Did you ever get a blood transfusion from a jack rabbit, Griff?"

"I got good blocking," Griff grinned. "That Johnny St. Hilaire got me ten extra yards."

Parmenter showed imagination in mixing up his plays. He called on Johnny St. Hilaire, the power plunger, and Johnny rode hard into the State line and carried to the fourteen. State got reinforcements and employed a 7-2-2 defense. Kenton went into pass formation and the home team's defense tightened up. The right end came in deep to rush the passer. State's secondary dropped back and Larry delayed, then took a shovel pass and headed for State's left side with Bill Griffith leading the way. He was pushed out on the State six-yard line.

Getting to his feet, Larry looked toward the Kenton bench. Most of the players were on their feet yelling.

"I can make a guess which ones are glued to the boards," Blimp observed dryly. "We score, pal, or break our necks trying."

State supporters implored their team to stand the Maroon off.

St. Hilaire hit State right in the mid-section where Blimp suddenly turned into a combination of a mad rhino and thrashing octopus. Blimp and Ollenbine opened up a hole that could have accommodated a moving van and St. Hilaire scooted through it and slammed over the last white line with three State tacklers hanging on to him.

Larry hurried over to where Blimp was slowly getting up. "What did you use in there, pal? A pickax?"

"Fundamentals was all," the center grinned. "Take that engi-i-ine off my neck. Is this good, Larry? This is it. This is what we've been dreaming about."

149

Larry saw the Kenton subs jitterbugging. Play was held up while a State first-aider worked over a man wearing the blue-and-gold jersey. A few moments later the lineman was helped to the State bench, and Kenton hopped quickly into line to get that all-important seventh point.

Parmenter held. Larry stepped into the ball and it sailed over the fingertips of a leaping State guard and split the uprights. The Kenton band blared forth with "Kenton Triumphant." St. Hilaire hugged Larry and whammed the flat of his hand against Blimp's shoulder. Bill Griffith, the happiest boy in the whole world for the moment, hooked an arm around Larry's neck.

"They'll have recovered from the shock now," Larry said as they spread out for the kickoff. "From now on this will be a sweet brawl."

"Up and at 'em!" Blimp yipped as Saresi of State gathered in Larry's boot on his twenty-one. Hirshmyer and Milholland were scampering downfield as though strafing planes were on their necks. Maroon tacklers converged on Saresi. They split through State interferers and got Saresi around the neck on the twenty-six.

State, deadly calm after the sudden storm, began a blistering offensive that slowly pressed the Maroon team back toward their goal line. Saresi and Fleck, and another fast-breaking halfback unleashed by State's coach, gradually ate up the yardage. It was bruising, all-out football, and penalties began to pile up. Larry and the others in the Kenton backfield began making more tackles than the line. At midfield, State took to the air lanes and a pass, Hitchcock to Greer, worked with beautiful precision on the Kenton twenty-eight.

Kenton rooters began pleading with the Maroon team.

On the next play, a thrust at the right side, Saresi drove through and bore down on Bill Griffith, two blockers clearing a path for him. The stands were in an uproar; a score seemed imminent.

The colored boy drove in and split the interferers with an impact that must have shaken the State coach's teeth. Saresi had to reverse his field and Larry had time to catch up and bring him down with a jarring thump on Kenton's twelve. Griffith, badly shaken up, fought against going out, but Blimp and Larry assured him that he would be back in before he knew it.

State's sympathizers gave the colored boy wild acclaim as he jogged toward the Maroon bench.

Pumps Kennard came into the Kenton backfield. Vince Pask took Ben Price's place. A substitute guard took over for the jaded Ollenbine. " Need some help, huh? " Kennard bit out.

" We do," St. Hilaire said tightly. " Got any with you? "

State turned the big guns loose. Fleck reached the Kenton secondary, and here Kennard took his blocker out and Larry stopped Fleck with a low tackle that dumped him back over Blimp's shoulders. A gain of one yard! Saresi came thundering in from a fake pass formation, and again Kennard was in there backing up his line, alongside St. Hilaire and Larry. Saresi failed to pick up more than half a yard. Larry helped Pumps up and the Pundit looked into his eyes for a moment and suddenly smiled. " Larry, did we smear that baby? "

" *We* sure did, Pumps."

Blimp slammed Kennard on the shoulder. The Pundit turned around.

" Oh, you! " Blimp chortled.

" It's O.K., Blimp. It's O.K.," Kennard said.

State's quarterback fired a pass into the coffin corner, but it was batted down by Johnny St. Hilaire. One more try for the touchdown. A State substitute ran to the field and the home cheering section turned loose full blast. The sub was Tolbert, field-goal specialist. He would have to kick from an angle.

The ball was snapped, and the State booter ran up and kicked. But an inspired Maroon line surged forward, and out of it and lifting himself high, came Sweetser. His upthrust hand deflected the ball and it flew wide of the posts. Larry heard faintly the disappointed groan that washed out of the stands. A State lineman had crashed into him hard and a lot of lights danced inside his head. There was a medley of voices in his ears, and out of it came Blimp's worried query, " Larry, you hurt? "

He got up, but there was a lump of nausea in the pit of his stomach. Chuck Gorcey came in to take his place. " Hit 'em hard, kid," he said.

Hunk slapped him on the back when he took his place on the bench.

Kenton began to move from its twenty-yard line. From a punt formation, Chuck Gorcey packed the oval on a spinner play. After faking to Kennard he slashed in at a hole in State's line vacated by the defensive tackle, and slipped and fell for no gain. He got up and slammed the ball down and kicked up a divot with his cleats. St. Hilaire put a hand on his shoulder and the back twisted away from Johnny and snapped a word at him. Larry watched Hunk. The coach had slowed the rhythm of his moving jaws.

St. Hilaire cracked State's line for three yards. Pumps Kennard dropped back to kick. He got it away and the State fullback gathered it in on his own thirty-seven and tried to bring it back within striking distance of Kenton's goal, but was driven out on his forty-four.

Fleck got three yards off tackle. Saresi, the work horse, hit the middle of the Maroon line and found Blimp Crocker as immovable as the pyramids. Saresi came tearing through the weak side on a trick play loaded with razzle-dazzle and Kennard and Johnny St. Hilaire met him, picked him up, and slapped him down. With only a yard and a half to go for first down and his team leading by five points, State's quarterback called for a punt. Fleck booted for State and the ball rolled out of bounds on Kenton's thirty-four.

Gorcey boomed in from the tailback spot on a fake reverse. He piled into his own interference at the scrimmage line and lost half a yard. He stood up to St. Hilaire, his jaws moving fast, and Pumps Kennard moved in and drew him away.

Hunk McQuade said: "Take Gorcey's place, Larry. Griff, go in for Kennard." He also sent four fresh linemen trotting in at the heels of the backs.

Chuck Gorcey slammed his headgear to the ground, picked it up and fired it toward the Maroon bench. The stands booed.

Kennard yelled as he ran off, "Stop acting like a kid, Chuck!"

Larry looked at the clock. There were twelve minutes of playing time left.

Blimp said: "Well, there's no rest for the wicked. Has Hunk forgotten he's got two other centers? I'm battle fatigued, pal. Ask me what day this is?"

"You love it," Larry said, and elbowed the fat boy in the ribs.

"That Vince Pask, as much as I hate to admit it, is playing a whale of a game, Larry."

"How about Kennard, Blimp? He never was so good."

"They see a chance to win," Blimp guessed.

"No," Larry said. "It is the old story of the house divided. Once it starts knitting together — Come on, time's in again."

"I guess you've made up your mind about Gorcey now," the fat pivot man said. "His own crowd is beginning to catch on."

The Kenton team stepped up to the line and Parmenter

153

began to touch off a drive that was to make history. He used Griffith where speed of foot and catlike agility were needed. When he had to have up to three yards for first down, he powered Johnny St. Hilaire through State's rapidly tiring forward wall. When the colored back showed signs of too much battering, he called on Larry. No spotlight for anyone. Team play. Co-ordination. Griffith, however, had caught the fancy of the big crowd. He had the home team's supporters badly worried, and they called upon State to stop the dusky, dangerous back.

After a play that netted nine yards with Larry carrying the ball, Blimp and Vince Pask got unscrambled. The ponderous center was almost sitting on the Pundit.

Pask grunted: " Get off me, you hippo, before I'm squashed like a melon. We sure opened up that line, didn't we? "

" Yeah, Vince." Blimp rolled off the big tackle. He looked at Pask, and the big Pundit suddenly realized he'd stepped out of character. His smile vanished, but his face remained friendly. He helped Blimp up.

" Thanks, pal. Don't it feel swell to act human? "

" Nuts to you," the tackle said, and quickly took his position.

The oval was on State's twenty-two-yard line. There was a lot of room toward the left side of the field, Red Parmenter told himself. He'd loosen up that State defense with a pass and then shake Griffith loose. One of McQuade's strategic charts clear in his mind, he took the ball from Blimp and shoveled it to Larry, and Larry faded to his right and looked for Hirshmyer. He threw it hard and the end leaped high, but failed to hang on.

Again Kenton lined up. State's secondary was looking for the pass. Griff catapulted around State's right end with three blockers and raced to the home team's eleven before he was belted down. He did not get up. Mike O'Doul came out, and the Maroon players rushed over and stopped Vince Pask when he aimed a punch at the State tackler.

"That was deliberate!" Pask raged. "They went out to get him."

Blimp grinned at Pask. "Now, why would anyone want to do a thing like that, Vince?"

The tackle cooled off and stared sheepishly at the center.

Blimp said: "Unity, that's the stuff we need. Singleness of purpose. That's what we've been after, Larry and me, for a long time, Vince. It's nice to see you standing up for Griff."

Larry felt good as he knelt over the colored boy.

"Just got whacked a little hard on the noggin, Larry," Griffith said. "I'm O.K. No need for Hunk to take me out this time."

"You've just about carried us this far," Larry said. "We'll go the rest of the way, feller."

Kennard trotted up after checking in. He looked down at Griff and held out his hand. "Mister, you're one sweet ball player. You go sit this last one out. We'll need you for the other games."

The State rooters gave the colored boy another tremendous ovation as he left the field. Standing in a shadow stretching out from the State uprights, Larry knew that more than one victory had been won by Kenton that afternoon. The Maroon would score, no doubt, but that was of secondary importance. An understanding had been born on this scarred field. In the face of State, a common, friendly enemy, Kenton men had forgotten differences and petty prejudices. Wardell had been right. Characters are formed on football fields.

Play got under way again with State's stands pleading for their team to stem the tide.

Larry, with Pumps Kennard and Johnny St. Hilaire blocking, bewildered State's defense on a fake reverse and pounded to State's three before he was smothered under a swarm of blue-and-gold jerseys. He was shaky when he got to his feet, but shook the fog out of his eyes. The sod seemed to undulate under his feet, and Blimp caught hold of him. " What's your name, pal? "

" John Smith," Larry grinned.

"Good. For a minute I was worried."

Pumps Kennard said: " O.K., Larry. Now it's our turn. Come on, Johnny."

State's forward wall braced. St. Hilaire, his head down, knees pumping high, hit the Blue and Gold right in the middle and clawed his way to the half-yard line. On the next play, with the whole stadium on its feet, Pumps Kennard tore off tackle, grunting like a big bullock, and was piloted by St. Hilaire and Blimp into the end zone for a touchdown.

On the bench, Hunk McQuade seemed to suddenly shed ten of his years. His eyes were filled with mist as he watched Pask hug Blimp Crocker and do a sort of *rhumba* with him. Pumps Kennard and Larry Barstock were wrestling big St. Hilaire around, and two other Pundits were trying to get in on the show. Beside him sat the colored boy, chuckling with happiness, and raving over those last two plays in which he had played no part. This was the Kenton that always should have been.

Chuck Gorcey leaned forward, his jaw muscles white, oblivious of the wild roar from Kenton adherents.

Here was a boy, Hunk thought, who tried too hard. Chuck had always played the game for himself. He had to stand a little above the crowd and be the center of attraction; otherwise he had no taste for the going. Up to now he had stood out in an inferior backfield.

Hunk said, " Go in and kick that point, Dekker."

The Pundit eagerly threw his blanket aside. Larry Barstock came running off and the Maroon cheering section shouted his name.

Dekker kicked the ball straight and true, and McQuade left him in there. He sent in six fresh players and smiled at Price, Ollenbine, St. Hilaire, Pask, and Milholland as they came over the side-line stripe. "Good work, men! It's as sweet a show as I've ever seen."

The scoreboard read: Kenton 14; State 12.

State had a little less than two minutes left in which to pull the game out of the fire. Saresi went back in despite a limp and smashed his way to his own thirty-one after picking up the kickoff. From there, State flapped its wings. The air attack frightened the Kenton section for a few moments, but Pumps Kennard intercepted a long pass on his forty and streaked for the side line. Dekker spilled two State tacklers with a rolling block on State's thirty. Blimp, still in for Kenton, got in the way of the last Blue-and-Gold defender in some inexplicable manner and Kennard raced over for the third Maroon score. Dekker again kicked for the extra point, and the Kenton bench went crazy.

The gun went off just as the ball was placed down for another boot by Kenton, and the State fans started pouring toward the exits, their glumness a thing that could be tasted. The final score: Kenton 21; State 12.

In the dressing room, Pask and Kennard and Dekker walked up to Bill Griffith a little self-consciously and thrust out their hands.

"Look out you don't get a shock, Pumps," Vince Pask grinned. "He's the spark plug."

Blimp's cherubic face wore a great pleased grin.

The bars were down. Hunk let his squad pour off the steam. He sat on the bench with them and soaked in the friendliness

157

and good feeling. He had gambled and he'd won, and he was fully prepared for the repercussions.

Mel Jardin came into the locker room, and his clothes seemed a little too large for him. He had been in the stands and he knew there would have to be a change in the policy of *The Kenton Opinion.* He saw Chuck Gorcey and went over to him.

"What's the matter, Chuck? Everybody's happy, aren't they?"

Chuck lost control. "What's the matter? Maybe you're deaf, dumb, and blind. I've been pushed off, that's what's the matter. I'm on the wrong side right now."

The shouting and horseplay subsided quickly.

"I came to this place to play football," Chuck fairly yelled. "That's about all I came here for. Touchdowns give a guy the inside track on a job when he's finished here. You guys never had to come up the hard way, and so you go for the rah-rah stuff. I majored in football, and I've flunked. You can have the books I shelled out good money for — at a bargain! I'm washed up and I'm clearing out. Next year, I'll pick a college that —"

"Nobody said you were washed up, Chuck," Hunk McQuade said. "There's room for you on this team if you care to take it. But we're not building a star."

"No? You're doing a good job with Griffith."

"He happens to be that good," Pumps Kennard cut in.

Gorcey, smoldering, headed for the showers.

Pask touched Larry on the knee. "I've been something of a rat."

"Maybe a white one," Blimp said.

"That guy," Vince laughed. "He's better than a shot of penicillin, Larry. We've been missing a lot in the Pundits, I can see that."

"Oh, I know I'm good," Blimp admitted.

158

Chuck Gorcey came out of the shower, dressed hurriedly, and started toward the door.

Larry called out: "Wait, Chuck. I'd like to talk to you. I —"

"Wrap it up," the ex-Canford Prep star said curtly, and went out and slammed the door behind him.

The sports experts called the Kenton victory over State the greatest upset in a decade and reached deep into the barrel for superlatives in describing the play of the team Hunk had apparently snatched out of nowhere. Ray Conahan's column, however, was significant if one took the trouble to read between the lines. The Boston writer did not share the apparent incredulity of his contemporaries. Hunk McQuade, his column said, had been long overdue, and not only in the development of a typical Maroon football team.

Two days before the game with Connecticut, Larry and Blimp received invitations to receptions given by three Kenton fraternities, Zeta Gamma, Sigma Phi, and Delta Epsilon.

"We are cordially invited, huh?" Blimp asked. "Looks like there is a change around here. One day we are impossible upstarts, the next—"

"A good chance to look them over and see what they stand for," Larry said. "A lot of fellows have rushed in too fast and found out they had nothing in common with the group."

"I don't know," Blimp said dubiously, "I like it here, Larry. Feels good too to know you can tell them all to go fly a kite after what they—"

"You're a spiteful cuss, Blimp."

"O.K., we'll go," Blimp growled. "I wish I had a mind of my own. Say, what'll we do with the little notebook?"

"Nothing. It's served its purpose, I think."

Leaving Blimp, Larry walked over to Standish, sacred precinct of the Pundits. He made a racket with the heavy brass knocker on the door, and a Pundit opened up and thrust his head out. "We've got a vacuum cleaner," the student said. "And we don't care if you do want to work your way through State college. We hate magazines — Why hello, Barstock. Don't you know *you* can't step over this sill?"

Larry laughed. "I certainly do. Chuck Gorcey around?"

"I think I saw him a minute ago. He was packing this morning. Wait here, and I'll see if I can find him."

Larry sat in an old chair on the porch. Five minutes later Chuck made his appearance. "What do you want? I don't think we have anything to say to each other."

"Why not, Chuck? Let's have a walk around the block. You know I'm sort of out of bounds here."

"Looks like that goes for me too," Gorcey said bitterly. "All right; but I've got to get back fast and finish packing. And don't try to sell me Kenton tradition."

"I just want to make everything clear," Larry said, going down the steps. "I want you to know, if you do leave Kenton, that I've never held any ill feeling toward you. You built up your present frame of mind inside your own head. I might have felt the same way if I'd been picked for the Pundits instead of you."

"What way?" Chuck asked defiantly as they walked down Mohawk Street.

"You know what I mean. If you walk out of here because of something that doesn't exist, you'll knock your future from under you. Hunk needs you. Anything can happen to me, or Griff, or Johnny St. Hilaire. You're a good player and you can still look ahead and say you were on the team that licked Vail three straight years. Forget you're a Pundit, even though it is a signal honor, and be Chuck Gorcey. Are Vince Pask and Pumps Kennard quitting?"

"They don't have to worry," Gorcey said as they turned

161

the corner into a side street. "They have jobs waiting for them when they graduate."

"With a Kenton diploma in your pocket," Larry said, "there's also a job for you. There's a thousand kids who dream about being in your shoes and you want to kick it all away. Don't do it, Chuck. Think it over, will you?"

Chuck was silent until they came back in front of Standish. His voice sounded a little thick when he said, "I'll think it over, Barstock."

Crossing the square graced by the statue of Kenton's founder, Larry met a group of Pundits, Mel Jardin among them.

"Hiya, Barstock," Dekker greeted.

"How's the educated toe?" Larry asked.

Jardin kept walking, his eyes fixed straight ahead. Dekker held back.

"Don't grab at those frat offers too fast," he said. "We have ideas of our own at the Pundits."

"Thanks. But that has to go for Blimp Crocker too."

"Blimp," said Dekker, and was silent for a while. "Well, we'll see."

Chuck Gorcey was on the Kenton bench when the Maroon played Connecticut. Once Hunk took the wraps off his miracle backfield, there was no question about the outcome. The Maroon led at the half, 27–0 and he sent Gorcey and Pumps Kennard in for the second half. Dekker was pressed into service when a long punt or a point after touchdown was needed. The Nutmeggers scored in the last quarter and threatened to repeat in the last two minutes. Kennard and Gorcey were in trouble over pass defense and Hunk sent in Griffith and Johnny St. Hilaire to relieve them. "And you go out and go to work, Blimp," he told Crocker.

"Knock those aerials down," Pumps said as he loped past the colored player.

Gorcey's eyes flashed a question as St. Hilaire gave him a friendly tap on the shoulder. He seemed to have acquired another two inches of height as he took the blanket tossed at him by Larry.

"Nice game, Chuck," Larry said. Hunk looked Gorcey over out of the corner of his eye.

"Three touchdowns today, Larry," Gorcey forced out. "You were hot."

Bill Griffith messed up a daring Nutmeg aerial on his twenty-four. The Connecticut quarterback faded back to midfield for a last try with half the Kenton team crowding him. He deliberately threw the ball away and drew a five-yard penalty for his team. That was the last threat on the part of the visitors and Kenton had won its fourth straight, 34–6.

A storm that had been gathering for several days finally moved into Stowbridge. The first signs showed themselves in the Kenton gym one afternoon when Hunk McQuade failed to make his appearance. Mike O'Doul paced back and forth and kept looking at his watch.

The players sat around. Fifteen precious minutes slipped by before a freshman invaded the sanctity of the varsity locker room. He handed a slip of paper to O'Doul, said, "No answer," and hurried out.

Mike read the message and then looked hard at Larry and Vince Pask.

"What's up, Mike?" Larry asked.

"I don't know, unless you and Pumps and Vince put that polka-dot bow tie on the statue last night. You three are wanted at the president's house as soon as you can get there."

Kennard took a deep breath. "I have a hunch," he said.

"So have I," Blimp sighed. "Oh, good-by new stadium. Let the termites be happy with the old."

"The rest of you get out there and play football," Mike ordered, "and make it snappy."

"We should organize," Blimp yelped. "We should go on strike."

"I'll strike you in a minute, Tiny Tim," Mike yelled at the center, "and you'll think you got caught at Hiroshima."

President Ryerson sat at a massive, mahogany time-scarred desk that had once been the property of old Joshua Kenton. Hunk McQuade sat in an armchair near the big windows, looking out over Prexy's perennial garden. There were four other men in the room, all middle-aged, and one of them was Big Bill Wardell. Larry grew weak at the knees.

Vince Pask said, "Dad!" and hurried across the room.

Pumps Kennard choked out, "Larry, it's the old boy!" And then he too, walked over and pumped the hand of a heavy-set man wearing horn-rimmed spectacles and a crisply trimmed mustache.

"You look fine, Pumps. Never saw you in better shape," Mr. Kennard said.

"How's mother, dad?" Vince asked. Larry heard the voices faintly. He felt naked and alone. He looked over at Hunk and the coach smiled ruefully.

President Ryerson quickly made the introductions. Larry's heart pounded heavily as he acknowledged the nod from the stern-faced man sitting near Prexy's desk. Mr. Lansberg! President Ryerson said, "Are we all seated, gentlemen?" and cleared his throat. "I've been aware," he began, "that we've had dissension of a kind here at the university, but I've considered it wise to keep hands off. I believed that my experience with young men taught me not to take their differences too seriously. Considering what has taken place here the last

164

week or ten days, I feel my judgment has been vindicated."
He glanced at the three varsity players briefly. "You boys
have been called here, if I may put it this way, as witnesses
for Coach McQuade."

Lansberg said suddenly: "You apparently do not consider
this a serious matter, Ryerson. I say it should be brought to
the attention of the board. There have been charges made
by certain students that question the integrity of prominent
alumni. The stories in the newspapers have been most humil-
iating to me, as well as to my friends. These students charge
that they have been discriminated against. It would appear
to me that McQuade believes their propaganda. He cannot
deny that he relegated members of the Pundits to the bench
in favor of players who were malcontents. Simply because
certain students qualified for an honor society — "

"Wait!" Hunk said, getting to his feet. "There's more to
this than 'simply because.' When I accepted the coaching
position here I was reminded very subtly that it would be
wise for me to lean over backward when it came to naming
players for the varsity. You were one of those men, Mr. Lansberg. Mr. Rossiter was another. I can name a dozen more
who weren't willing to pit their sons against open competition and who wanted the Pundits to control Kenton football.
Their promises to add certain buildings to the campus were
the clubs over my head."

"Now, look here!" Lansberg shouted. "I won't — "

Vince Pask got to his feet. "We've settled all this among
ourselves," he said, staring at his father. "I'll admit I wrote a
letter home I shouldn't have written, but two days later I was
sorry for it. I won't stand by and let even my father put the
hooks into Hunk. Larry, have you got that little notebook I
lost?"

"No, Vince. I never intended to use it. Not in the way you
thought."

165

"Well, it would show these gentlemen how the Pundits tried to control every activity at Kenton, and tried to prevent non-Pundits from reaching places of any importance, wouldn't it?"

"I'm leaving it where it is," Larry said.

Vince went on: "We deserved being benched. That State team would have murdered us. You won't get a word out of me against Hunk McQuade. He's been fairer to us than he should have been."

After an uncomfortable silence, Mr. Kennard said, "Pumps, do you agree with that?"

"I certainly do, dad. As Vince said, we're settling everything ourselves. We've got a great football team; we've been set straight; and everything at Kenton is under control."

Prexy sat back in his chair and smiled faintly.

Big Bill Wardell remained silent.

Lansberg stubbornly held out. "I am not in sympathy with this adolescent reasoning. I shall most certainly look into this further and will withdraw my offer to the university if — "

"If what, Mr. Lansberg?" Hunk cut in. "If Kenton doesn't continue with discrimination and snobbery? The new stadium, I understand, was to be a memorial to your son. Do you think he gave his life for discrimination?"

The room was still.

Hunk McQuade went on as though talking to himself. "Money can do terrible things to a man's heart and soul. I know what the highest salary ever paid to a coach in these New England States almost did to me. I shall be very glad to leave after we've beaten Vail."

Hunk's words lingered in the big room. Lansberg sat slumped in his chair, his eyes fixed wrathfully upon the coach. And then, slowly, his expression changed and he sighed deeply and looked down at the floor.

Big Bill Wardell spoke at last. "Gentlemen, I've learned

166

a lesson. I like what I've seen and heard, and I don't see why we need to press this business further. Our generation is a little presumptuous, I think, in attempting to straighten out the differences of the new. Remember the mess we made of it? We came here to pull down a mountain and we stuck our fingers into a molehill." He walked over to Larry and the halfback rose to his feet.

"It looks as if I picked the wrong man, Larry," Big Bill said, and held out his hand.

"Chuck is going to turn out all right," Larry assured him.

"I expected you to say something like that."

Lansberg said, "Gentlemen!" and everybody turned and looked at him. He coughed and was plainly ill at ease. "I know when I'm licked," he admitted. "McQuade, is that miracle team going through its paces this afternoon? I'd like to look it over."

Prexy said, "I've never enjoyed a more wonderful afternoon."

"I'd like to look at the team," Lansberg repeated.

Larry and Big Bill Wardell went out together. "I've got to step fast, Sir," Larry said. "I can get in a half hour's practice."

"I had a hunch I'd slipped up that night," Wardell said ruefully, "but show me a man that's never made a mistake and I'll show you a failure. Would you like to join the Pundits?"

"I'd like to think it over, Sir," Larry said and didn't believe his own voice.

In the locker room, Pumps Kennard laughed. "Did you see the expression on my old man's face? He looked as though he'd swallowed a bug."

"Mr. Pask, if you happened to notice," Vince said, "could have been knocked over with a duck's tail feather. Big Bill put it very nicely in a few words, didn't he?"

"Hunk was pretty good himself," Larry pointed out.

167

Hunk McQuade stepped in with Wardell. " Get out to the field! " the coach roared. " You take longer to change clothes than a woman."

The three players hurried and said, " Yes, Sir," in unison.

Hunk gave them a meaningful side glance before he walked out, chewing calmly on his gum.

CHAPTER
18

Three days after Kenton's impressive win over Manhattan, Larry wrote his father:

" *Thanks for the ten bucks. I guess you've been wondering what happened here since the State game. It was just a matter of misunderstandings getting ironed out almost over night.*

" *Never mind what you've heard and read about Blimp and me. We're not the advance agents for Better Worlds, Inc. The misguided group of Pundits knocked themselves into line. They put the spotlight on their own shortcomings by trying to magnify ours, and they sent out a lot of noisy chickens that finally came home to roost. In other words, they threw stones through the windows of their own greenhouse. Blimp's philosophy must be catching. Anyway, everything is pretty swell now, and believe it or not, I've actually heard three pretty big men admit they were wrong.*

" *My marks are up to snuff, so tell mother not to get any gray hairs. What would you think if I joined the Pundits? They're setting out lines. Maybe I'll be satisfied to stick with any one of the good frats as long as Blimp comes along too. The guy is still the same morale stiffener and I don't know what I'd do without him. If he isn't named for an All-American berth before he's through here, I'll never stop wondering why.*

" *You should have seen him against Manhattan. Hunk Mc-
Quade calls him the Crock of Gibraltar. And Griff, the colored
boy! It's a terrific team and we ought to take Vail and be the
first team at Kenton to go through a season unbeaten and un-
tied since 1936. My knee gives me no trouble. Give my love
to mother and Susan. Don't drive yourself too hard because
the Barstocks wouldn't know how to act with a million bucks
in the bank anyway.*"

Larry was sealing the letter when Blimp and Johnny St.
Hilaire barged in. Blimp looked doleful.

" Why the gloom? " Larry asked. " Your face is longer than
an Eskimo winter."

Blimp dropped into an easy chair that squealed and
groaned under his poundage. " Johnny and I were talking on
the way over here. We figure things are too good to be true.
You can't make a new dog turn over and play dead the first
day you get him. Yeah, remember when the Yugoslavs got
smeared. A lot of them took to the hills or hid in cellars and
struck back."

Johnny St. Hilaire said: "He's got something there, Larry.
I'm thinking about Jardin, Kyle, Platt, McKnight, Brewerton,
and Dobell. They're too quiet and haven't committed themselves. That Jardin is the kind of guy who'd pull the temple
down over his head if only a few of us got conked along with
him."

" I don't see what harm he can do now," Larry argued.
" The die-hards generally fall into line sooner or later."

" Maybe," Blimp grunted. " Maybe, I say. But leopards
never had any luck with newfangled spot removers. And
don't forget something else, Larry. The Board of Trustees and
Ryerson aren't exactly boon companions. Prexy has clashed
with them a couple of times and they might love to sink the
old hatchet into his classical skull."

170

"They're grown men," Larry said impatiently.

"Which is what worries me," Blimp retorted. "A lot of grown men act like grammar-school kids. Just read the newspapers or go down to Washington sometime and listen to the politicians."

"Maybe they should elect you a senator," Johnny St. Hilaire scoffed.

"Maybe I wouldn't do so bad," Blimp said tartly. "Anyway, I wouldn't try to hog all the marbles in the game."

Shortly after five o'clock the next evening Larry and Blimp and Johnny St. Hilaire, after a bruising session on the practice field, walked into Commons and found a bespectacled student sitting in the hall. He looked familiar to the varsity players and Blimp suddenly snapped his fingers. "Sure, he's the printer's devil from *The Kenton Opinion*, Larry. What can we do for you, Horace? We have very little time if you want an interview, so make it brief, my good man. Now my solution for the Far Eastern problem is this — "

"This is not a joking matter," the student said. "My name does not happen to be Horace. It is Frederick Smalley. I must talk to you fellows where we can't be overheard."

"Come on upstairs, Freddy," Larry said.

They ushered the representative of *The Kenton Opinion* into their room.

Smalley said: "I have here a copy of the *Opinion* that appears tomorrow. I believed it my duty to bring it to you. It is incredible, and I remonstrated. Jardin, however, intends to go through with it."

Larry winced at the headline.

KENTON ALUMNI SCOURGED BY VARSITY COACH!
McQuade Admits Complicity in Football Scandal

"It's hard to believe, even from Mel Jardin," Blimp whispered over Larry's shoulder. "Well, I warned you."

171

Jardin, Larry soon discovered, after scanning the first paragraph of fine print, had denounced the very system at the university that he had helped to build.

The scourging, Jardin had written, had taken place behind the closed doors of President Ryerson's study at his residence on Maple Avenue. The *Opinion* believed it to be its duty to bring the matter to the attention of the Board of Trustees and the alumni lest the deplorable practices of control by a privileged few become deep-rooted again at Kenton.

" Any of these papers gone out, Smalley? " Larry asked, his face white.

" I do not believe so," Smalley said.

" Jardin knows this will finish him at Kenton," Blimp said hoarsely, " but that won't worry him in the least. He will be considered a sort of martyr, a sacrificial lamb, a fearless editor who put the truth above all else. To spite us, he's willing to sell Kenton down the river. Why, there mightn't be a Vail game again for five or ten years."

" Larry, we've got to do something quick," St. Hilaire cried.

Larry nodded. " Those papers are still at the *Opinion* office, Smalley? O.K. — let me think."

" I know where there's a delivery truck," Blimp said.

Larry gave him a sharp glance.

" At a garage outside of town where I stopped to get gas a few days ago when I borrowed Pumps Kennard's coupe."

" Think the guy would let us have it? "

" For five bucks? I bet! "

Larry said: " Hunt up Pumps and Vince, Johnny. Bring them here. Did Jardin have any reason to think you'd spill this, Smalley? "

" I don't see why he should."

Blimp went to the window and looked out. Three fellows stood out there on the walk, but they weren't Jardin men. St. Hilaire hurried away and Blimp plunked down on his bed

172

and shook his head. " If I ever have a son, Larry, and he wants to be an editor, I will smother him in his sleep."

Larry walked up and down the room, the damp copy of the *Opinion* clutched in his fist. " Jardin is not a real editor. Don't make that mistake, Blimp."

" His kind keep the world the way it is," Blimp insisted. " Are we taking that bunch of tripe? "

" What do you think? If we don't we'll lose all we've fought for and won since coming to Kenton."

Blimp blew on his knuckles. " I hope we get resistance."

" It's got to be done quietly," Larry warned. " You keep that in mind, and also remember to keep your tongue tied down."

Twenty minutes later Pumps Kennard and Vince Pask followed Johnny St. Hilaire into the room.

Pumps was raging. " Johnny told me, Larry. Let's see that rag of Jardin's."

" To think we'd string along with a heel like that," Vince moaned.

Pumps read Jardin's story and flung the paper to the floor. " When do we go to work? "

" You have a key to the place? " Larry asked Frederick Smalley.

" Yes."

Larry was suddenly smiling. " Pumps, you and Vince pick Johnny and Blimp and me up around nine o'clock. We'll ride out to the garage and get that light truck if we have to steal it. Watch out for Jardin's bunch. I think you know who they are."

Vince Pask nodded.

Larry said, " Blimp, get that little notebook out from under the floor board and give it to Vince."

" So that's where you kept it," Pask said ruefully.

Larry said: " Better go now, Pumps. You too, Freddy, and

173

let me tell you something. If they handed out medals for distinguished service at Kenton, I'd see you got one. Better go out one at a time." He picked up the newspaper and began tearing it into bits.

Vince struck a match and touched the flame to the little notebook and dropped it into the empty wire wastebasket. "You'll have to admit the thing came in handy, Larry."

Late that night, a light delivery truck purred through the deserted campus, ran along the street in front of Greenough, turned left a block farther on and finally stopped in the rear of Standish Hall. Larry and Blimp got out first. Larry inserted Smalley's key into the lock of a door and turned it very slowly. He pushed the door open and stepped inside. Pumps and Vince followed Blimp, leaving Johnny St. Hilaire to keep watch outside.

They advanced along a dark hallway and came to a door that wasn't locked. When they went through it, they found themselves in a small storeroom where a single electric light bulb burned. There was a sudden movement in a corner of the room and a startled voice called, "Who's — ?"

Larry, leaping toward the sound, bore the boy to the floor before he could cry out. He held his hand over the mouth of Jardin's sentinel and applied a hammer lock that dragged forth a painful grunt.

"It's George Kyle," Larry whispered as Blimp came over to lend assistance. "Start loading those bundles. Work fast. Now take it easy, Georgie, or I'll break your arm."

Fifteen minutes later, the storeroom was empty of copies of *The Kenton Opinion*. Larry had let up on the hammer lock and was kneeling beside the subdued Kyle.

"Go through the entire office with a fine comb," he ordered. "Ransack it. Be sure we don't leave any loose copies around."

"I wish I could slug somebody," Blimp sighed. "Try and make a break, will you, George?"

174

"You won't get away with it," Kyle choked out.

"What'll you bet?" Blimp asked.

Pumps called, "Let's get out of here."

"Sorry, Kyle," Larry said. "We have to tie you up."

They bound Kyle's wrists and ankles.

"You'll be a little cramped, palsy-walsy," Blimp gloated, "until Jardin lets you loose. The ropes are not so tight that your blue blood will stop running."

Vince came out of the office. "I don't think we've left one copy behind, Larry. Pumps and I'll call on Mel first thing in the morning, just in case he has one or two copies under his mattress."

"This is unconstitutional, you know that?" Blimp asked with mock gravity. "Gagging the press and stifling free speech. Who's got a big handkerchief?"

"Where'll we dump the stuff?" Pumps asked while Blimp wound the handkerchief around the lower part of Kyle's face.

"Glug-ug," Kyle protested.

"Such language," exclaimed Blimp.

Larry shoved Blimp toward the door.

Johnny St. Hilaire was fidgety. "About time. Let's get far away from here."

The truck's engine stepped up as the night prowlers climbed in. They heard someone shout as they swung away from the curb.

"Andy, the watchman," Pumps said. "He'll let Kyle loose."

"I've got a hunch Georgie'll keep his lips buttoned," Blimp stated. "He'd probably like to finish his education here. We'll all be missing at bed check and Hunk'll go nuts."

"After we show him a copy of the *Opinion?*" Pumps scoffed. "Sure, we keep one for Hunk and perhaps another to show Prexy. Where are we taking this load?"

"The Stowbridge dump," Larry said. "There's always fire

175

smoldering there. By morning there won't be any of this trash left. How much for the delivery truck, Blimp? "

" Eight bucks. I tried to beat the guy down, but no soap. This inflation — "

" The cost is nothing," Vince Pask cut in. " I'll take care of it."

When they reached the dump Blimp held his nose. " Smells almost as bad as this load of newspapers. All right; let's pile out and unload."

At two o'clock in the morning Pumps Kennard's coupe let them out on the edge of the campus near the power plant. Larry and Blimp kept under the trees until they came in sight of Commons. Then they ran swiftly across a triangle of lawn, up the steps, and into the old house.

" Whew-w-w! " Blimp gasped. " I won't be worth a nickel in scrimmage today." He lumbered up a flight of stairs. " They made a good fire, didn't they? "

At nine-thirty, Pumps stopped Larry in a corridor outside the chemistry lab. " We called on Mel Jardin two hours ago, Larry. He had most of his stuff packed, and I think he'll be on a train before noon. Vince — well, I tried to stop him, but he poked Mel a couple. We found three papers in his room. We turned the joint upside down."

" Kyle? " Larry asked.

" I met George at breakfast," Pumps told him. " He doesn't know from a thing, and he knows he'd better not. I'll see you around, Larry. About those forms in Jardin's print shop. We didn't think to — "

" I have some cuts coming to me," Larry said. " I'll hop over there with Blimp in about fifteen minutes and take care of that. Seen Hunk? "

" Not yet. Are you worried? "

" Not with what I've got in my pocket. I'd better be hopping into the lab."

176

All that day an air of mystery hung over the Kenton campus. Where was *The Kenton Opinion?* Was there any truth in the report that Mel Jardin had suddenly left Kenton? Had a delivery truck been seen going past Greenough Hall in the dead of night? Had anyone actually seen a fight in the sacred confines of the Pundits?

"Reminds me of the day the atomic bomb was dropped," Blimp said to Larry as they headed for the gym that afternoon. " It was so and it wasn't so. Well, we'll see how much Hunk knows in a couple of minutes. I have a hunch he's testing out the old horsewhip."

" Jardin got on the train at Stowbridge with his luggage at eleven thirty-seven," Larry said. " That much I do know. Johnny St. Hilaire was down there."

Blimp held out his hand. " Shake, pal. What more do two guys have to do to get the Nobel peace prize? "

Mike O'Doul and Embree, McQuade's assistants, waited until the entire squad was present. Mike said: " There are certainly some popular guys around here. Once more their presences are requested. Barstock, Crocker, Kennard, Pask, and St. Hilaire. The coach will see you upstairs in his office. And don't keep him waiting. He's in a nasty mood."

The five students filed up the stairs, walked the length of a corridor, and stepped lightly into McQuade's office. The coach tossed aside a sheet covered with diagrams. " Sit down! " he said coldly.

They sat down.

" What time did each of you turn in last night? "

" I think you already know," Larry said.

" I sure do. You all know the training rules? "

" We had very important business, Coach," Blimp said.

" It must have been. Well, don't gape at me like goldfish. Out with it."

Larry walked over to Hunk's desk and laid down a copy of *The Kenton Opinion*. Hunk picked it up and stared. He looked at the football players, then back at the paper again. He let a word slip out no one at Kenton had heard him use before. His lined face seemed to purple.

"That's where we were, Coach," Larry said. "There were about ten thousand of those papers. They're ashes now over at the city dump. Jardin is heading for home."

Hunk put the newspaper down. "When did you get tipped off about this?" he asked, suddenly quiet.

Larry told him.

"Sure there's no more of them around?"

"We are," Pumps Kennard said positively.

Hunk took a long deep breath. When he looked at the players again he gave them a wry grin. "O.K., run along. And thanks for everything." He placed the newspaper in a drawer of his desk and turned a little key in a lock.

Walking slowly back down the stairs to the locker room, Larry wondered if Hunk included more than just the taming of Jardin in his thanks. He hoped that he and Blimp had helped open up that hole in the line of least resistance for the coach. But no matter what the cause, all that mattered was that Hunk had made his comeback.

Four minutes had gone by in the Vail Bowl. Fifty thousand spectators had been on their feet for most of those four minutes, for this was a dream game between teams packing explosive power in the backfields and possessing rock-ribbed forward walls.

Kenton had taken the kickoff on its five-yard line and had driven across midfield and deep into Vail's territory. After Griffith had plowed to the Blue's thirty-two on a beautiful cutback, the Maroon had suffered a holding penalty on the next running play. Vail had stiffened and had intercepted a pass on its twenty-nine. The Blue had then shown its terrific power, combining a running attack and an air offensive that finally came to grief on Kenton's thirty-nine because of two successive off sides.

The Maroon had Griffith, Barstock, and St. Hilaire. Vail was countering with Raffberg, Bronzek, and Lohrman.

And now Bronzek punted for the Blue, aiming at the side line. His boot was rushed and the ball slithered out of bounds on the Kenton thirty-one. The Maroon lined up quickly, starting its attack from a double wing.

Larry balanced himself on the balls of his feet and looked across the crouching lines at Vail's secondary. Tom Barstock was up there in the seats with Susan. Mrs. Barstock never had had the courage to watch a football game.

Parmenter called the signals clearly. It was to be the fullback off tackle.

Blimp passed. Bill Griffith, as soon as he felt the ball slap against his hands, stepped diagonally backward as if to pass, and waited until interference formed. Suddenly he drove forward, gathering speed with every step, and smashed inside Vail's defensive end. Two Maroon linemen and Johnny St. Hilaire were the protective screen as the dusky boy swept around for eleven yards.

The next play was a double reverse, Griff to St. Hilaire to Larry. With nice blocking, Larry carried it inside the Blue end and then swung sharply to the outside. Bronzek drove a blocker back into his face, and Larry reversed his field and was picked up by Raffberg and halted. Blimp helped him up.

"What day is this, pal?"

"Pretty grim, huh?" Larry grunted. "What do you think?"

"We win," Blimp said.

There was a yard and a half to go for first down. Parmenter sneaked it himself, boring into the Blue wall behind Blimp, who crashed against Vail linemen like a hippo gone berserk. Vail's coach sent in three new linemen, and Hunk McQuade removed Pask and put in Ben Price. He also replaced Hirshmyer with Spahn at right end and rushed in two fresh guards. The chips were down.

Bill Griffith got the ball and faked it to St. Hilaire, completed a full spin and catapulted inside the strong side of the Blue left tackle. The play was piled up, with Bronzek and Raffberg coming in to back up their first line of defense. Griff did not get up and the Maroon trainer came running from the bench. A groan welled up from the Kenton cheering section.

The colored boy was finally lifted to a sitting position. He grinned up at Larry, but his eyes were foggy. He reeled when they let him try to walk on his own, and Pumps Kennard came in and took over for him.

"We'll be seeing you later, Griff," Blimp called after the departing colored fullback.

180

"Sorry," Bronzek said to Larry and St. Hilaire.

"O.K.," Blimp grunted. "It's no tea party. How's *your* health?"

Parmenter decided on razzle-dazzle. He called for Hunk's scoring play, number 87, with Larry carrying the mail. It was a combination of a sweep outside the Vail right end and a lateral. The interference carried Larry around. Blue tacklers dove for him as he cut sharply to the left and flipped the ball to Pumps. Kennard continued the end sweep with Johnny St. Hilaire knocking Bronzek over, but the big back was forced out of bounds on Vail's seven.

Now it was all St. Hilaire. He crashed off tackle for three yards. He hit the Blue forward wall in the middle and fairly rolled off Blimp Crocker's big back to land on his angel bones on Vail's three. The Blue asked for time out. The going was now lumpy and for keeps. The Maroon offense did not resent the recess. Blimp and Larry and Pumps flopped down.

"Quite an outfit," Pumps said. "They expected something out of the hat. Deception. We handed them the orthodox punch and they're on the ropes."

"I wonder did Susan see me sneak Red Parmenter to a first down back there," Blimp gasped. "Say, I'd better talk to Red right now."

"What's on Blimp's mind?" Pumps asked Larry.

They found out in the huddle.

When he hopped to his position, Johnny St. Hilaire looked a little beaten, and seemed to favor his right leg. Pumps dug in his cleats and wiped his hands on his maroon jersey. It was a bad habit of a lot of good backs, a telegraphing that they were to carry. Raffberg fell for the gag beautifully, pointed toward Kennard and the Vail players watched him.

The crowd's roar stretched thin as Blimp bent over the ball. Parmenter crouched behind him. Blimp passed and then powered his way into the big Vail line, his head down and his

183

feet pumping. Kennard and St. Hilaire got in behind Parmenter and added impetus to the quarterback's drive.

Hunk McQuade, for the first time since the opening whistle, was up off the bench.

There was a tremendous pile up. When it cleared, Blimp was on the goal line. Red Parmenter was half on top of the ponderous center and just inside the end zone. Fifty thousand fans let loose a deafening roar as the official threw up both arms. Kenton had scored.

Sage trotted in from the Maroon bench. Behind him came Felch, the second-string center, and Dekker to try for the extra point.

"We're going to get it, Red," Blimp panted. "Hunk'll pin our ears back."

McQuade did. "What kind of cockeyed, half-witted play was that, Red? What hit you, a sunstroke? The temperature is only about forty-two above out there. You, Crocker — "

"It seemed the thing to do," Red said. "You saw Kennard wipe his hands on his chest? So they were expecting Pumps. Johnny St. Hilaire was faking the bad leg."

"I talked him into it, Coach," Blimp said, and stopped long enough to watch Dekker add the seventh point for Kenton. "It was imagination, Hunk."

McQuade seemed about to choke. Suddenly he dropped his arms to his sides. "Sit down, Crocker; save your energy." His jaws started working normally on his gum again.

Vail struck back. Getting the ball on their eight, they launched Raffberg, Lohrman, and Bronzek. Kenton gave ground stubbornly, slowly.

With his team on the thirty-nine, fighting to hold the Blue from getting six yards on the next two tries, Hunk sent Gorcey in to replace Larry. Dekker was still in, in place of St. Hilaire. It was a Pundit backfield once again, but it had a spark that had not been there at the start of the season.

184

The clock said three and a half minutes to go for the first half. Vail had to quicken its tempo or walk off trailing, 7–0.

Bronzek hit the Kenton strong side for three yards. The spectators expected Vail to go into punt formation and Kennard dropped back in safety position for the Maroon. It was a punt formation — but Vail had elected to gamble. The player in the kicker's position, Raffberg, tossed a bullet pass out in the flats where a Vail end gathered it in and ran to Kenton's twenty before Chuck Gorcey caught him from behind.

The home crowd thundered and set up that age-old clamor for a touchdown.

Again Vail passed, a center alley shot that clicked to Kenton's thirteen.

McQuade said: "Crocker, Barstock, Price, Wellstood, Inman. Get in!"

Bronzek carried for four yards against the strengthened foe. Raffberg got two more on a spinner. The Maroon was desperate. Bronzek smashed toward Ollenbine and the guard charged with mighty force and knocked the defensive guard right into the ball carrier for a loss of a yard.

Blimp slapped Ollenbine on the back. "Very nice, Olly!"

Lohrman was in motion for Vail. The ball was snapped and the Blue quarterback faded quickly to the right. The Maroon line seeped through and at him and he had to get the ball away fast. He fired into the end zone and Larry leaped high and tipped it away from the jumping Vail end's eager fingers.

Yards yet to go and only a few seconds left in which to make the touchdown. Bronzek tried for it and fought his way forward with all the power and leg drive he could muster. The Kenton line buckled, then snapped back and Bronzek was smothered under a heap of blue and maroon on the goal line.

Kenton supporters held their breaths. Bronzek got up and the official signaled no touchdown and pointed toward the Vail goal.

A tremendous Kenton cheer lifted toward the sky.

The Maroon lined up for the offensive on their four-inch line!

Deep in his end zone, Dekker kicked. The oval was caught on the Kenton thirty-five by Raffberg who battered his way back for eleven yards. Just time for one more play. The Blue hurriedly lined up. The quarterback faded back ten yards when he took the ball from the center and threw a long one into the end zone. A Blue receiver caught it, and for a moment, Kenton's rooters groaned.

A spectator cried: "There was a horn on the play. Looked like Vail was off side."

The officials confirmed the fan's diagnosis and the Maroon cheering section roared. The half ended with that play and the teams trotted off the field.

"Who's running this ball club, Parmenter?" Hunk McQuade roared at the redhead in the Vail gym, still thinking of the unorthodox play that had set up a score.

"You, Coach," the quarterback said. "But I'm in charge of the team when it's out there. I read in a book you wrote once about a quarterback you had out in Ohio. You said he was the greatest opportunist you ever saw."

"You ought to have more sense than to read those books," Hunk countered lamely. "That was six years ago. You pull another one like that, Red, and I'll walk in there myself and drag you out by the seat of your pants."

"We only needed three yards to score, Hunk," Blimp called out. "I figured he could ride me pickaback that far."

"A mastermind," Hunk threw at Blimp. "What do you do with it when you go into math class, check it?"

"My big mouth!" Blimp groaned.

186

Mike O'Doul busied himself among the jaded and begrimed players, devoting most of his time to Bill Griffith. The colored back insisted he was all right. Doc Cullop, however, kept asking him questions, and kneading the back of Griff's neck. Two assistant managers poured tea into paper cups and passed them around.

"I'll take lemon in mine," Blimp said. "No, make it milk and sugar. Oh, if you insist, I'll take it straight."

Larry laughed. He straightened his face as he caught a glimpse of Chuck Gorcey. Chuck, he knew, had in the long ago built a picture in his mind of a player stealing the show in a great football game such as this and he would be the guy who would run almost the length of the field for the deciding score while thousands cheered and shouted his name. Chuck had discovered that it took more than one man to beat eleven other college players, and the chore of simply being an essential part of a human machine was still a bitter pill for him to swallow.

Hunk picked a newspaper off the floor and turned to the sports page. After a swift glance at a headline he said to Mike O'Doul: "Conahan is the only writer giving us a chance today. He's a pretty good prophet all around." He tossed the paper away and stood up and signaled for quiet.

"I know you can take this game. You have the courage and the power, but what is more important you have confidence in yourselves. You made mistakes in the first half, but I know you won't make them again." Hunk paused and smiled dreamily as if somehow these words also applied to him. "Look for the breaks, because they'll settle this game. I'm starting the same line. In the backfield will be Kennard at full, Barstock at right half, St. Hilaire at left half. Sage, you'll do the quarterbacking."

Chuck Gorcey kept staring down at his shoes. He did not look at McQuade.

Hunk had spoken only of Kenton's power to take this game, but the fifty thousand people in the stands knew the Blue had the capacity to score sooner or later.

From the spot where Bronzek gathered in the second-half kickoff, Vail moved downfield for seventy-four yards without relinquishing the ball. It was a slow, bruising, and relentless advance along the ground broken up only once by a short pass play. Saresi and Raffberg refused to be denied.

Hunk McQuade gave Larry a rest. He took Price and Ollenbine out and then bent forward, chin cupped in his hands, and watched the Blue batter its way to the Kenton four on a tricky reverse play. From the four Bronzek crashed over for the score, fairly hurdling the Maroon wall. Raffberg kicked the extra point and it was all even.

Kenton tried to roll back. With St. Hilaire and Kennard bearing the brunt of the attack, the Maroon reached their thirty-four and at that point drew a clipping penalty. Back on their nineteen they were forced to punt. Again Vail unleashed terrific power and again tore the left side of Hunk's line to bits. The Blue smashed to the Maroon seventeen, then cut loose with an aerial that was caught beautifully by the Vail left end in the end zone.

Larry groaned on the bench. He watched the Kenton front line surge forward and block Raffberg's attempt for the point after touchdown. Was this going to turn into a rout?

"All right, Barstock," Hunk said. He turned loose five reserves, and sent Parmenter in to relieve Sage. "All right, Chuck."

"Am I glad to see you, pal," Blimp gasped when Larry came up to him. "They're murdering us."

"We'll see," Larry said grimly.

Gorcey ran back Saresi's boot to his own twenty-nine, and Larry gave him an encouraging slap on the back when he came into the huddle. The fourth quarter was now under way.

"It's up to us to get within striking distance, Chuck. Hunk is holding Griff for the kayo. The guy's all right."

Chuck nodded and tried to force a smile. He was expected to help set the stage for a star, a stage on which he had expected to shine. He remembered a dinner in the Westbrook Prep gym and wished he was living that night over again, knowing then what he knew now.

"Let's go," he said gruffly.

The Kenton machine did go. Kennard cracked viciously off tackle for seven big yards to spark the drive. Pumps carried again and made it first down on the Kenton forty-one. Sage hung out a clothesline with Milholland on the other end and the Maroon was over the midfield stripe by seven sweet yards. Vail subs came in.

St. Hilaire got four through the middle. Then Larry hit between guard and tackle on Vail's weak side and found himself shaken loose in the Blue secondary with only big Bronzek between him and an open field. He tried to fox the Vail back by cross-stepping, but Bronzek got him and tossed him hard on the Vail thirty-six-yard line.

Time out for Vail.

Bill Griffith trotted in for Kenton and the Maroon cheers cut through the imploring thunder of the partisan crowd. The Kenton band opened up.

Larry knelt beside Blimp. The center had been in there all the time.

"Tell Susan I died facing the enemy," Blimp choked out. "Write my dear mother — "

"Even if you are out on your feet, Hunk'll leave you in here for us," Vince Pask mumbled. "Hot or cold you're quite an obstruction."

"Raffberg's gone out," Larry said. "He twisted a knee."

On the first play, after the game was resumed, Larry carried to the Vail thirty-one on a tricky spinner. The sky suddenly became black as Bronzek hit him. The stands caved in and there was a mighty sound in his ears like a river breaking through a dam.

After a while Larry opened his eyes and looked up at Griff's big smile. The colored boy said, "You go over and tell Hunk we'll make this touchdown."

"Yeah," Blimp said. "You talked to yourself for a few seconds there. Who is a gal named Sheila?"

"Sit this one out, Larry," Johnny St. Hilaire said. "Here, Chuck, give us a hand."

Larry went off and the field seemed to keep spinning around and around. He guessed his father and Susan had lived through a few bad moments up in the stands.

He sat down beside Hunk and watched the Maroon hop up to the line. He held his breath and dug his nails into the palms of his hands when St. Hilaire was stopped with no gain as he tried to go through Vail's right tackle. Time was of the essence.

Sage banked on Griffith.

The colored back took off like a rocket on a cut-back play. Gorcey and St. Hilaire went to work on the left side of the Blue line, isolating the end and tackle. Blimp, despite his bulk, moved around in back of his own linemen and spilled Bronzek, who was aiming for Griffith.

Griffith picked up his blockers on the other side, but Gorcey lost his footing and three tacklers swarmed over the dusky back. They knocked him off stride but he kept going, pivoting like a ballet dancer, and started forward again. He reversed his field and walked a tightrope to Vail's fourteen before he was finally banged out of bounds.

Johnny St. Hilaire had to be picked up. "Go in there, Pumps," Hunk said. His jaws were not working on his gum.

Larry, still jarred from head to heels, dimly saw the Maroon organize for another thrust. The shouts of the multitude were

190

far away. *The best of luck to you all, and my only regret is that I can't send the whole bunch of you to the Pundits. It has been wonderful to be here tonight —*

Bill Griffith was through Vail's line again and snake-hipping through a host of Blue tacklers. He was a dusky phantom, a will-o'-the-wisp, an artful dodger. He crossed the ten, the five, and was hauled down on the three.

Certain men who lost their lives in this last war . . . who prepared at Westbrook. . . . I can hear certain voices still — and certain laughter —

The stands were one great roar of sound.

Griff was getting set. Larry thought of distant fields he had seen on a silver screen, fields gouged by the caterpillar tractors of war machines because of the selfish ambitions of a few men. Now, as Sage gestured toward the banked stands to be a little quiet, his head cleared and he looked out at the scarred turf of the Vail oval where, in a few seconds, Kennard and Gorcey would help a colored boy toward that goal. Not just Vail's goal, but the goal a Negro star had set for himself.

The signals rang out sharply.

It is almost new, yet older than these surrounding hills — new because it has hardly ever been used. That rule is the Golden Rule.

The continuous roar shook Larry through. He saw Griff cut wide around Vail's left end on a surprise play. A human blanket covered him. Blue tacklers tumbled over the sod. The colored boy cut in quickly, bounced away from a rolling block, and fell into the end zone for the tying points.

Kenton's shrieking rooters tore up souvenir programs and newspapers and threw fistfuls of makeshift confetti high into the air. They screamed Bill Griffith's name, and Hunk Mc-Quade chewed slowly on his gum with a beatific look in his aging eyes.

Gorcey came running to the bench. The Maroon had at

191

last climbed to the heights and something told Larry that the ex-Canford Prep star had climbed with them.

Larry said, " Great blocking, Chuck."

The stands became very still. Vail's line charged with all the fury left in it as the ball was snapped. Dekker ran up on the oval and kicked it from under Sage's fingers. It cleared the wildly flailing fingers of Blue defense men and lobbed lazily over the crossbar.

Kenton 14; Vail 13.

There were not quite two minutes left. Vail spread out to receive the kickoff, but Larry, on the bench close to Hunk, knew that the Blue was finished. Kenton would not lose now. The team was a team in every sense of the word. It had licked a tougher foe than Vail before it had invaded New Haven. It had licked prejudice and selfishness. It was not going to be pushed back now.

Vail tried desperately, but the Maroon line was impregnable. Millionaire's son, farmer's son, janitor's son stood side by side and threw back the powerful thrusts of Bronzek, Raffberg, and Lohrman. A final desperate touchdown pass, thrown from midfield, fell untouched on Kenton's ten-yard line and bounded over the side-line stripe as the gun went off.

The Kenton team gathered at midfield and whooped their joy. They regained a semblance of control and huddled to give Vail a great cheer. Then they broke and swarmed toward the bench where Hunk McQuade stood, the beatific look now completely covering his weathered face.

Larry threw his blanket away and ran to meet the team and found Chuck Gorcey running beside him.